Political Issues in Nursing:
Past, Present and Future

Political Issues in Nursing: Past, Present and Future

Volume 3

Edited by

ROSEMARY WHITE, SRN, SCM, OHNC, MSc, PhD
Independent Researcher and Author,
History of Nursing,
East Stratton, Winchester, UK

A Wiley Medical Publication

JOHN WILEY & SONS
Chichester · New York · Brisbane · Toronto · Singapore

The Library of Congress has cataloged this serial publication as follows:

Political issues in nursing.—Vol. 1- —Chichester; New York:
  Wiley, c1985-
    v.; 22 cm.—(A Wiley medical publication)
  Annual.
  ISSN 0883–4504 = Political issues in nursing.

    1. Nursing—Political aspects—Periodicals. 2. Nursing—Government
policy—Periodicals. 3. Nursing—Social aspects—Periodicals. I. Series.
    [DNLM: 1. Nursing—trends—periodicals. 2. Politics—periodicals.
3. Public Policy—periodicals. W1PO241J]

RT86.5.P62   362.1′73—dc19   86–647500
AACR 2   MARC-S

British Library Cataloguing in Publication Data

Political issues in nursing: past, present
  and future.
  Vol. 3
  1. Nursing services—Great Britain—
  Administration
  I. White, Rosemary
  610.73′068   RT89

  ISBN 0 471 91256 5

Phototypeset by Input Typesetting Ltd., London SW19 8DR
Printed and bound in Great Britain by Biddles Ltd., Guildford

List of Contributors

MARIE L. CAMPBELL, RN, BA, MA, PhD, Research Fellow, Faculty of Social Sciences, Carleton University, Ottawa, Canada.

DIRK M. KEYZER, RGN, DANS, MSc, PhD. Projects Co-ordination Officer, Welsh National Board for Nursing, Midwifery and Health Visiting, Cardiff, Wales.

JENNIECE LARSEN, RN, PhD. Professor and Director, School of Nursing, University of Manitoba, Winnipeg, Manitoba, Canada.

JUDITH LATHLEAN, BSc. (Econ.), MA. Freelance researcher in nursing, lecturer and writer in the role of trained nurses and continuing education for nurses. Formerly Research Fellow, Nursing Education Research Unit, Chelsea Campus, King's College, University of London, London, England.

JILLIAN M. MacGUIRE, RGN, BA, PhD. Research and Development Officer, Elderly Care Unit, Mid-Staffordshire Health Authority, Stafford, England.

JEAN ORR, RGN, RHV, BA, MSc. Lecturer in Nursing, Dept. of Nursing, University of Manchester, Manchester, England.

SHIRLEY M. STINSON, RN, Ed.D., LLD. Professor and Associate Dean, Faculty of Nursing, and Professor, Dept. of Health Services Administration and Community Medicine, University of Alberta, Edmonton, Alberta, Canada.

JANET L. STORCH, RN, MHSA, PhD. Associate Professor, Dept. of Health Services Administration and Community Medicine and Associate Professor, Faculty of Nursing, University of Alberta, Edmonton, Alberta, Canada.

ROSALIE THOMPSON, RN, RM, DNE, MPub.Adm., BSoc.Sc. (Nursing). Professor and Head, Dept. of Nursing, University of Cape Town, Observatory, Cape Town, South Africa.

ROSEMARY WHITE, SRN, SCM, OHNC, MSC, PHD. Independent researcher and writer on the history of nursing, East Stratton, Winchester, Hants, England.

Contents

Series Preface

This is the third volume of a series which we hope will fill a need in international nursing circles. There was a time, possibly, when nursing was a simple occupation located in small hospital units or communities and could be maintained by minor adjustments in policy decisions—the gentle touch on the tiller. Those days have been overtaken and nursing now is a complex society, far more complicated in its structure than most other comparable occupations. Decision-making has, therefore, assumed greater meaning and now takes place at a distance from the practitioner: it involves the government, a bureaucracy and political and fiscal considerations. Nursing is now shaped by politics but we have been slow to accept these factors and to develop a more sophisticated and worldly understanding of them.

Traditionally, the history of nursing has been written and taught as a celebratory exercise, useful in the socialization of new entrants to the occupation, as a means of imbuing them with an ideology of service and dedication. It has been written at a very elementary level, as a chronological narrative of events, highlighting leaders and their achievements, emphasizing the progress of nursing from the early, untaught practitioners to an honoured profession regulated by statutory controls and its own institutions.

This type of history has tended to repeat and reinforce many myths and, therefore, to sustain a traditional base which is not susceptible to closer inquiry. It has become the core of a particular form of reality which is learned by old and new nurses and which, then, colours their responses to change.

In recent years nurses have begun to examine their history with more critical eyes and, thus, to open it out to re-interpretation and fresh analysis. If the results of this new look are not always flattering, they do encourage a new perspective and a more objective reality from which policy may be drawn for the future.

History has a social purpose—more than history for its own sake. Politicians and policy-makers often appeal to the past for guidance or justification. Because evolution does not consist of self-contained jerks, it seems preferable to try to understand the present by understanding the past and how it took its form.

History has another, more practical, use: it teaches us the craft of analysis, it is an intellectual discipline, directed towards searching for meaningful answers. There are, of course, many different types of history. A history of nursing could address itself to the study of the role and functions of the nurse or the development of nursing procedures, and so on. This series is directed towards the study of policy and politics in nursing.

Although the study of social administration is a well-entrenched discipline and has been much concerned with the development of social policy, it has not so far concerned itself with nursing policy. This is an area which has, so far, been as invisible as nursing itself has been described. This series is aimed at redressing that omission.

Historically, nurses have been regarded as 'local' labour, with little need for national policies of recruitment and manpower planning. This has meant that policy decisions have not been subject to scrutiny, follow-up or evaluation. The surge in the scope and cost of health-care has made necessary a re-evaluation of the cost of employing nurses, but this is being effected without much understanding of the consequences of that policy. Decisions are being taken as unique episodes, detached from the broader context and lacking a conceptual orientation or understanding. It is hoped that this new series will help to redress that.

Social policy choices are made through political processes, grounded in the several institutions of government. These processes have not received enough attention from nurses, who have remained on the periphery of policy-making. Since most countries have made the decision to set up hospitals and health-care systems, nurses tend to accept that their position in these decisions is a *fait accompli*. This is not so, and it is hoped that we shall be able to demonstrate how nurses are affected by, and can affect, social policy.

Lastly, we are conscious of a small but growing number of nurses all over the world who are studying macro-policy and nursing politics, often in considerable isolation, lacking collegiate support or even understanding. Although the organization of health-care systems, nursing and political systems differ between one country and another, nurses already understand that there are many similarities and that international intercourse and exchange can offer greater understanding and support. We hope that this series will foster those by acting as a focus, putting like-minded students in touch with each other's work and facilitating its publication. In furtherance of this aim, the series editor will welcome correspondence from readers.

R.W.

Introduction

This is the third volume of this series, *Political Issues in Nursing: Past, Present and Future* and the last that I shall be editing. The series was originally started to fulfil, and encourage, a need in international circles. That need was to enable students of nursing to publish work which took a political view of our 'profession'. Many journals, at the time when this series first appeared, declined work which examined nursing from a political point of analysis on the grounds that it was either non-scientific (a pretentious view which displayed all the artless immaturity of self-conscious scientism) or that it was too contentious. Other journals, more open to innovative thinking, were crowded with submissions and not able always to find space for this new type of study.

Since this series started, the climate has changed and nurses have become more freely able to express politically oriented views. That is not to say that we claim any cause and effect in this movement but we can claim that the series was timely and that the need was there to be satisfied. If at the same time we have also encouraged others to start to think politically, we shall be all the more content.

Nurses all over the world are trained and educated differently. Their process of socialization, therefore, differs from one country to another and their affiliations to their profession vary. In some countries the emphasis is on academic preparation and nurses are taught to think for themselves and challenge received knowledge and philosophies. In other countries nurses are trained by dogma and procedures and are indoctrinated with the 'right' ideas which inhibit their critical faculties. In most countries nurses are trained (or educated) to think of nursing as a unitary occupation with a single value system and a professional association which fights by negotiation for their rights and status. Almost by definition, nurses all over the world are motivated by altruism, even if many are also now endeavouring to match this altruism with an equal injection of natural rights.

There is, however, a tension—even a conflict—between altruism and rights which has been ably discussed by Susan Reverby:[1]

Caring is not just a subjective and material experience; it is a historically created one. Particular circumstances, ideologies, and power relations thus create the conditions under which caring can occur, the forms it will take, the consequences it will have for those who do it.

Most nurses, their employers and the general public still remain rooted in the nineteenth-century Nightingale ethic of caring as a duty which 'undermined a direct assertion of the right to determine that duty'[1] and which, therefore, continues to insist on serving others subserviently. However, the world has changed since Nightingale, and individual rights have come more and more to be recognized, even by governments and legislators. Since late in the nineteenth century, women's rights have also slowly come to be more acknowledged although many would claim that this movement has not developed quickly enough. A training in 'discipline, order and practical skills'[1] does not need to equate with a life of subservience, and many nurses today are beginning to urge that 'the creation of the conditions under which it is possible to value caring and to understand that the empowerment of others does not have to require self-immolation':[1] Altruism with Autonomy.

The struggle for professionalism also takes different forms. Indeed, 'professionalism' means different things to different people in different parts of the world. In the US[1] and Britain[2] the major nursing associations turned to unionism in order to gain power. Concurrently, the American Nurses Association (ANA) looked at raising educational criteria to a first degree (baccalaureate) level 'as the credential necessary for entry into nursing practice'.[1] In Canada, the same target is being sought[3] but in Britain, the Royal College of Nursing (RCN) and General Nursing Councils (GNCs) sought for professionalism (that is to say, power) by trying to buy it with reduced educational entry levels.[2]

As Reverby,[1] Campbell[3] and White[2] have shown, professionalism meant different things to the worker nurses. It meant to many nurses, workplace skills and the capacity to supply the needs of their patients or clients. For other nurses, again, it meant decent wages and working conditions and they saw no contradiction between demanding these and being of service to those in need of their caring.

There has, therefore, arisen in many countries a separation between the nursing organizations, who seek for power to uphold their leadership, and their membership who seek for the right to care within their own terms, be it within a functional authority or an authority founded on skills and a knowledge base. There is still lacking a common strategy in nursing and this must persist if nursing is to develop the type of care that society demands and continue to recruit the different levels of nursing staff which that care requires, since nursing is not a unitary society with a common value system. It is a pluralist society with a variety of value systems which a single association or trade union cannot adequately represent. Those associations which have turned to trade unionism cannot, by their very nature, continue also to represent the values of the professionalist nurses; neither should the associations which aspire to learned society status seek to represent the generalists or managers amongst nurses. In an occupation as broadly based as nursing, there is a need for different types and styles of representation for the respective composites.

The institutions and nursing leadership are, therefore, defensive and worried by analysis of their policy-making. This is not an unnatural reaction. Whilst they become more and more politically active and call for more lobbying by their members, at the same time they fear and discourage political individualism.

Many journals are dependent on the support of the powerful nursing associations either for the provision of information, insight and news or for advertising and other financial benefits. Those journals are, consequently, chary of publishing or of reviewing contentious articles and are highly selective in their choice. Nurses who are courageous enough to embark on political studies risk further support, funding and, even, their jobs in seeking to publish their findings. This series has not sought only for controversial contributions; indeed, we have wanted to maintain an even-handed and open-minded selection. The field of policy analysis in nursing is, however, still a new field and it requires a particular turn of mind to pursue. It requires the student to emerge from her acceptance of nursing dogma, the framework of duty within which she has been socialized and a passive acceptance of the traditional routes and goals taken by our leadership, to question how nursing is structured and organized and to pursue to their logical ends the policies within which nursing and health care are bandaged. If our findings are uncomfortable to readers, so are they to us; if they are painful, they have caused us pain too, for we are as rooted in our profession as are those who read our work. Our altruism and wants for our clients, and nursing, are no less than those of our colleagues. Indeed, it must be argued that perhaps they are greater since we have risked more in exposing our work.

The fact that this series has succeeded, and will be continued, and is widely read, must demonstrate that there is a 'silent minority' whose needs we are also fulfilling. Perhaps, by reading these volumes they, too, will be able to develop a way of examining policy-making and searching for possible outcomes. Many may not agree with our arguments but there are also many who may understand that the world of nursing has different realities and that it is neither 'disloyal' nor deviant to differ from their leadership nor to seek to influence policy-making in their own ways.

This volume contains many divergent views but, interestingly, since there are nine contributors offering nine approaches, there emerges a single, common theme. Each chapter comments on the bureaucratization of nursing and health care and its consequent dehumanizing effects. All the contributors make a cry for something (they tend to vary in their description of the 'something') to be done to re-establish the recognition of the individual in caring, and all give a sense of uneasiness—to say the least—about the preparation of the nurse to meet new challenges as we enter another paradigm of health care with its economic strictures, aging populations and illnesses that, so far, defy cure. If the authorities are not yet aware, the authors show an alertness to the demands and responsibilities that these conditions will put on good nursing.

Larsen opens this volume with a study of how power is obtained and how it can be translated into efficacious action. She offers an agenda for nurse leaders to follow in seeking to influence health-care policy for the achievement of nursing goals. She proposes that the nurse at the bedside can be a prime source for shaping the public's image of nursing and more active interest in helping to further the better education and preparation of nurses as well as nursing's aspirations for health care. Interestingly, although her references are predominantly drawn from Canadian sources, her analysis of the derivations of power are very similar to those of White. Larsen calls for nurse leaders to take a greater part in public policy-making and proposes that they should be better prepared for this.

White sees the problems of professionalizing nursing, that is to say of establishing a core of nurses with a sound knowledge base and a philosophy of providing for the individual needs of their clients, and of nursing taking greater influence in policy-making at all levels, as arising from the historic ideology of unity and its organization as a single occupational society. She calls for nursing to be regarded more as a public service with several structures for recruitment, training, promotion, payment and conditions of service similar to those of the civil service or armed forces.

Storch and Stinson discuss the proletarianization of many professions by the process of rationing resources and services to their clients, the bureaucratization of professional systems and the division of labour which divorces the skills of the worker from the execution of his work and so destroys his craft. They relate all these to nursing and find that, as with doctors, psychologists, pharmacists and lawyers, nurses have suffered equally. They observe that while there is a growing need for the nurse to take greater responsibility, her knowledge base and authority have not kept pace and her current role does not permit her to give attention to the humanistic dimension of nursing care. They describe this as a dysfunctional, disintegrative force since the state of the nursing profession and the social need for nursing service are no longer in a good functioning relationship. They find that the policies of nursing leadership impede effective nursing practice. Storch and Stinson see current professional goals, constrained by the bureaucrats, as distancing the nurse from the patient and they argue that deprofessionalization should allow her greater freedom to re-establish the social mission of nursing by enabling her to return more closely to the patient.

Campbell sees a division of interests between the leaders who seek to professionalize nursing via management systems with a strong economic orientation, and the working nurses who seek to maintain their own standards in spite of those management systems. She finds that the nurse academics in Canada, and the nursing leadership, have adopted male-dominated criteria in their own search for status and that the goal to raise nursing's professional standing through academic qualifications, which are determined by masculine values, serves to pass on to new recruits management values rather than nursing values. This is causing a rift between the Canadian nursing associations, who support this goal, and the working nurses whose own feminine goals and values are being endangered. She argues that in the process of trying to professionalize nursing, the nursing associations and nurse teachers have abandoned professional values for the sake of rational, scientific, accountable systems. Campbell also argues that in this process, nursing is not only losing its traditional feminine attributes but also its nurses.

MacGuire, in contrast, advocates the use of similar systems involving patient-dependency studies to determine the needs of the patients and staffing and skill-mix ratios. She argues that these systems, employed with nursing values rather than management values, can help the nurses to bargain for resources and withstand administrative pressures for greater productivity. MacGuire relates the nursing use of these systems to the care of old people outside NHS wards. Although this is commonly described as being 'in the community' their care may be in social security residential homes, private residential homes or nursing homes. Although in the UK these last establishments are inspected and have to be licensed by the health authority, MacGuire complains that there is no common standard for this, neither is there any process or policy for determining the need for progressive dependency care. There is no financial policy, in social security payments, for paying for progressive care and there are not enough nurses trained in this type of care to fill all the places required for the registration of a nursing home. She makes a plea for co-operation between the NHS nurses responsible for inspecting these homes, their owners or managers, and all those who work in them, to use the supportive model of care and dependency that she has described, to establish greater independence for the elderly and to give them the degree of care as they need it.

Keyzer agrees that nursing's clinical role is, in any case, blocked by rationing of resources and a medically controlled structure, geared to cure rather than care, and which is antithetical to the nurse's practitioner role and to better, holistic care. He, too, finds that management values constrain the nurse in her attempt to give patient-centred care. He discusses the organizational structures which maintain the status quo in roles and examines different organizational models of care which locate power in different actors in the setting. He proposes a theory for patient-centred care based on a 'codes and control' model as a means of redefining the role of the nurse towards the clinical. He, also, calls for a reorientation of nursing values towards the practitioner rather than those of a bureaucratic hierarchy.

Orr, too, calls for more holistic care grounded in the needs of the client rather than in male-dominated policies around which the system is shaped. She describes women's groups which are organizing self-help and seeking to influence health care policies. Working with these groups, nurses have had to adjust their own received goals and learn to work in partnership with their clients rather than in a hierarchical relationship which is traditional to health care.

Lathlean has found that newly registered nurses are ill-prepared to cope with their responsibilities on the wards. She discusses two schemes of post-registration development which, she argues, benefit the employing authorities as well as the nurses. She has found that there is, in England, very little continuing education for trained nursing staff. The two experimental schemes which she followed demonstrated how much the nurses benefited from them but she also observed the interrelationship between nursing aims and organizational policies. Lathlean raises the question of which nurses should be selected for this kind of continuing development and discloses that very few British nurses have had the opportunity to take part in any such programmes.

Thompson's chapter is interesting since it exposes to us the development and complexities of nursing and nurse education in South Africa. It has been written under the constraints of South African censorship regulations and an interpretation of the official statistics that she provides makes demands on the reader.

There are four and a half times more blacks than whites in the South African population; 1.7 times more whites than coloureds. The standard of secondary education for blacks is inferior but the rise of numbers of blacks in higher and further education in the last 20 years appears to be 7.6 per cent, while that for whites seems to be 1.2 per cent. Proportionally, black nurses have taken greater advantage of the distant learning opportunities provided by the University of South Africa (UNISA) for post-registration qualifications. She does not say if this is because of the greater difficulties they have in gaining admission or funding for full-time study at residential universities. Not surprisingly, more blacks (62.0 per cent) live in rural areas than do whites (11.30 per cent) and the range of health problems is divided between the modern diseases of affluence and old age and the older paradigm of infectious diseases and diseases of poverty. Thompson describes the problems of providing health care to a population widely dispersed in rural areas and proposes that, because of these and other circumstances, South African nurses have a mandate to take a much wider range of responsibility for their clients than do most nurses in the Western world.

There appears to have been a general decline in recruitment figures for all sections of the population but, especially, of black nurses. The ratio of black nurses per head of population is below the WHO standard but has improved over the past 20 years. That for whites is six times better.

She describes the struggle by South African nurses to separate nurse education from the service needs of hospital. Although this has now been achieved, it must be noted that two-thirds of the members of their statutory controlling council are appointed by the government. In spite of this, there appears to have been a steady improvement in the educational preparation of nurses, although the poor secondary schooling of blacks appears to disadvantage them in this respect.

South African nurses live and work in a difficult and complex society and, since they are not members of the International Council of Nurses, are isolated from their colleagues in other countries. Thompson's chapter gives us an opportunity to gain some insight into South African nursing and the political climate in which they function.

While each of these chapters adopts a different approach and discusses varying themes, the emerging plea appears to be for greater respect for nursing and nurses, for greater value to be given to care and the carers and for a better preparation for nurses to meet the needs of modern society. If nurses are seeking for greater autonomy and political power, it is in the search for a more caring society. If, as Reverby[1] proposes, the caring experience is a historically created one and is shaped by the contexts under which it is practised, then the systems in which nurses must function should be adjusted to allow them greater scope to meet the needs of society today. Nurses are not naturally political animals: they seek power only to be enabled to practise according to their lights. But since caring has historically been regarded as woman's unpaid labour, it has come to be seen as a duty: 'the duty to care, organised within the political and economic context of nursing's development, has made it difficult for nurses to obtain this moral and, ultimately, political standing.'[4]

At a time in history when, in a growing number of countries, individual rights are, at least technically, recognized, at a time when international politicians find it expedient to make great play in pressing for human rights, nurses still have to struggle for theirs, not just from their employers and their medical colleagues, but also from their own leadership, the representative associations and their nurse managers.

We also see the different approaches and use of the term 'profession'. In the end, writers in this volume seem to want to professionalize, or deprofessionalize, nursing in order to counter the goals of their leadership. Nurse leaders have sought for power to achieve the goals of their associations and, in doing this, they have sought to spread the membership of those associations more and more widely. But in doing that, they have recruited nurses with widely different values and cannot now adequately represent all of them. To most nurse leaders, the term 'profession' seems to imply a status of power: for the greater control of nursing and the better to influence policy-making, either by governments or by employing authorities. For the majority of nurses, the term 'profession' seems to imply a functional status with adequate and appropriate material rewards. For a minority of nurses, the term 'profession' implies a status of authority and recognition from other disciplines in their work, founded on a legitimate knowledge base and skills.

Each of these groups searches for professionalism but each seeks for something different: hence my description of nursing as a pluralist occupation. With different goals, each group employs different strategies, as we see in this volume.

This ambiguity of objectives and strategies leads to the conflicts that we also discern in this volume, although there is a persisting ideology of caring which helps to bind the groups together in a common occupation. The combination of cultural cohesion and conflict together form a tension which can only be healthy and constructive. A policy of unity leads to the preservation of the status quo. A tension permits growth and change by allowing new groups and new ideas to emerge. In a healthy pluralist society, there should always be a tension between the prevailing group and the countervailing groups. In nursing, we have been slow to recognize this as we have almost universally, it seems, been socialized into the concept of a unitary occupational society. This being the case, we have failed to recognize the several value systems operating within that occupation and, therefore, tend to sow confusion and, even, alienation, when we call for unity. We should acknowledge the unity of an ideology of caring and altruism in the whole occupational society of nurses, but we must learn to differentiate between the needs of the several subgroups of that total occupation. We must not confuse the unity of our occupational ideology with the pluralism of goals and value systems. If we fail to recognize this complex structure in nursing we shall fail to meet the needs of an increasingly complex modern society which we seek to serve.

It is only by examining our history and analysing our policies, which together shape nursing all over the world, that nurses can understand 'the educational philosophy, ideological underpinnings, and structural position' which have led us where we are today and from where we have to move forward.

ROSEMARY WHITE

References

1. Reverby, Susan, 'A caring dilemma: womanhood and nursing in historical perspective', *Nursing Research*, 1987, **36**(1) (January–February), 5–11.
2. White, Rosemary, 1985, *The Effects of the NHS on the Nursing Profession: 1948–1961*, King's Fund Historical Series, 3. King Edward's Hospital Fund for London, distributed by Oxford University Press.
3. Campbell, Marie L. see Chapter 4, this volume.
4. Fernberg, Joel, *Rights, Justice and the Bounds of Liberty*. Princeton University Press, Princeton, 1980. Cited by Reverby, 'A caring dilemma'.

Political Issues in Nursing: Past, Present and Future, Volume 3
Edited by R. White
© 1988 John Wiley & Sons Ltd

CHAPTER 1

Being powerful: from talk into action

JENNIECE LARSEN, RN, PhD
Professor and Director, School of Nursing, University of Manitoba, Winnipeg, Manitoba, Canada

During the past decade, the topic of power and politics has been a recurrent theme both in nursing literature and on agendas of nursing conferences. The time has come to push this discussion forward—to an examination of the nursing profession's involvement in shaping public policy. The purpose of this chapter will be to discuss selected factors that influence effective participation by the leaders of nursing organizations in the public policy-making process. To accomplish this purpose the concepts of policy-making, power and political resources will be discussed. Throughout the chapter, an agenda for being powerful— for moving from talk into action—will be identified. The underlying assumption is that involvement in shaping public policy requires active, visible participation in the political process. Active, visible participation necessitates the effective use of political influence to persuade government officials and elected politicians of the 'correctness' of nursing's point of view on public policy issues.

Public policy-making

Public policy-making is not simply a matter of problem-solving, or taking some common goal and seeking the 'best' solution. Public policy-making is a matter of choice in which the resources are limited and in which goals and objectives differ and cannot easily be weighed against each other. Influencing public policy involves conflict, negotiation and compromise. There are very few 'pure public goods', that is goods which are available equally to all citizens. Most 'public goods' distributed by governmental agencies confer differential benefits—some people get more than others; some pay more than others. The most important question to ask in understanding the public policy process is Lasswell's question: 'who gets what, when, and how?'[1]

The study of public policy-making is a rapidly expanding field of study and practice with new journals, new think tanks, new academic programmes and new organizational roles. For the purpose of this chapter, Thomas Dye's observation that public policy is 'whatever governments choose to do or not to do' will serve as a definition.[2] Dye drew our attention to the fact that both decisions and non-decisions represent policy. The decision of a government (or a governmental agency) to ignore an issue is a policy decision if only because the status quo is perpetuated. The never ending study of nursing education by various provincial governmental departments in Canada is an example of a non-decision which favours the status quo.

Bruce Doern and Richard Phidd, two of Canada's leading experts in the study of public policy-making, have suggested that public policy results from the interplay of ideas, structures and process.[3] Structures are organizations, bureaucracies and institutions from both the public and private sectors. The combination of structures involved in a policy debate is shaped by the issues being debated, by the particular context in which the debate occurs, and by the effective distribution of power within the governmental machinery. Nursing professional associations like all other interest groups in Canada tend to adopt organizational structures compatible with those of federal and provincial governments. The people who head these structures are the elected and appointed leaders of Canadian society. During public policy decision-making, various combinations of leaders are engaged in the process of ranking, balancing and allocating scarce resources of money, expertise, energy and time.[4] The importance of effective leadership of nursing's organizations deserves much attention as the nursing profession contemplates the exercise of power in public policy-making. How do we provide for the appropriate education of leaders for effective involvement in the public policy-making process? The first item on the agenda for action is the development of strategies for the political education of nursing leaders.

The processes of public policy refer to the changing dynamics which occur when leaders try to sort out the uncertainty created by the limits of knowledge, the lack of causality and by the political calculation of public and private reactions to suggested policy initiatives.[5] Observing the processes involved with attempting the most minor changes to Canada's health care system, either at the provincial or federal level, provides excellent and frequent examples of the risks, the uncertainties and the constantly changing environmental factors which are integral to the development of public policy. These are not negotiations for the faint of heart or the weak of spirit. And it is within these negotiations that nursing leaders must attempt to influence public policy.

Doern and Phidd observed that these structures and processes are imbued with the central ideas of the political culture of Canada and of particular Canadian provinces.[6] The ideas are central elements of public policy representing dominant values of the Canadian society. In the analysis of any public policy field, nursing leaders must differentiate different levels of normative content. Doern and Phidd hypothesized a three-level typology:[7]

(1) Ideology

An ideology is an umbrella of belief and action which provides political and social identity. Ideologies are an important element of the political culture of a country. While the ideology does not automatically lead to policy actions by the government in power, the ideology helps to foreclose certain policy options or alternatively to support the present course of action. Ideologies help screen out approaches which are unacceptable or which will be considered only as a last resort.[8] The major ideologies in Canada are liberalism, conservativism and socialism. Nursing policy initiatives must take into account the ideological preference of the government of the day— particularly in terms of planning strategy. For example, when making arguments to a left of centre government concerning university education for nurses, stress could be placed on the desirability of ordinary working nurses having access to higher education; while with a government having a right of centre ideology emphasis on the individual nurse's responsibility for excellence would be wiser.

(2) Ideas and paradigms

The second level of normative content is dominant ideas and para-digms. In Canada the dominant ideas include concern for: efficiency;

individual freedom; equity; stability; redistribution; equality; regional diversity; unity and integration.[9]

These ideas influence the political debates and the evaluation of public policy alternatives regardless of field. These dominant ideas are each considered desirable and are often totally or partially contradictory. The need to balance, order and allocate scarce resources to a set of contradictory ideas in the same policy initiative is a central aspect of public policy-making in Canada. In addition to dominant ideas, the second level of normative content encompasses major paradigms which influence policy fields.[10] A paradigm provides a series of assumptions which guide decision-making within a given policy field. Paradigms often become entrenched and thus change very slowly. An obvious example of such a paradigm is Keynesian economics in the field of financial policy. Since the late 1970s monetarism has emerged to challenge but not replace Keynesian economic principles (at least not in Canada). Similarly, health-care policy is dominated by the medically oriented curative approach, while the alternative paradigm espousing preventive ideas has gained only marginal political support. The dominance of the medical paradigm in the field of health-care policy should alert nursing leaders to the importance of having nursing experts on major national and provincial committees to gatekeep and to spread nursing's message if we are serious about our support for alternative health-care policy paradigms.

(3) Objectives

The third level of normative content is the specific objectives to be achieved within a policy field.[11] Specific objectives often concern the inclusion or exclusion of certain groups or categories from various initiatives.

The identification, understanding and manipulation of the three levels of normative content by nursing leaders is absolutely essential to the exercise of power in the public policy-making process. With few exceptions, nursing leaders have not been visible in public policy-making at the national or provincial level in Canada. When the media covers a local health-care issue, such as budget cutbacks at the hospitals, how often does it seek a nursing perspective? Equally important, do nursing leaders respond to the media request with a nursing point of view on the issues of concern?

To influence the public policy process, leaders of organized nursing must elbow their way into the front row of the public and private debates that result in new policy initiatives, at least in a few major policy arenas, for example in health care, in higher education, in women's issues and in labour relations. Inaction or invisibility by the leaders of organized nursing are not in the public interest and are certainly not in the best interest of the nursing profession. The public interest will be best served by nurses collectively and individually talking with politicians and the general public about nursing policy ideas and about the consequences of various policy choices, or governmental decisions, on the quality of nursing practice. The next item on the agenda for action is to elect or to hire nursing leaders who understand the public policy-making process and who are willing to be visible participants in the process.

Exercising influence

Involvement in the public policy-making process by nursing leaders necessitates that they have some resource of power that is used to influence events. A long distance separates the potential for influence from the exercise of influence. Mintzberg, in his book *Power in and Around Organizations*, suggested that trying to influence a social system is a three-stage process: (1) nursing leaders must have some resource of power, that is coupled with (2) some expenditure of time and energy in a (3) politically skilful way.[12] These are the three basic conditions for the exercise of power in the public policy process. Power may be defined as the capacity to influence outcomes in the public policy-making process. Mintzberg pointed out that the French word *pouvoir* means both 'power' and 'to be able'.[13] Power is the ability to get things done and to make things happen.

Sources of power

While there are a number of well-known formulations about the sources of power (for example Raven and Kruglanski[14]) the author has chosen to draw extensively on the work of Henry Mintzberg. The reason is related to the additional insights provided by his theoretical ideas. Mintzberg suggested that there are five general sources of power. Three of these sources are the control of (1) a resource, (2) a technical skill, or (3) a body of knowledge.[15] To serve as a source of power the resource, the skill, or the knowledge must be *essential* to the functioning of the social system.[16] Not only must the source of power be essential, it must be *concentrated* in the hands of a small number of people who are prepared to co-operate with each other, and this knowledge or skill or resource must be *non-substitutable*.[17] It must be irreplaceable. Control of a body of knowledge, a technical skill or a resource that is essential, concentrated and non-substitutable creates a dependency by various aspects of the society on the people who control these sources of power. This type of power is based in a dependency by organizations or groups or individuals on that knowledge, skill or resource.

One of the most important sources of power is the control of an essential, concentrated and non-substitutable body of knowledge or professional expertise—the knowledge of the medical practitioners performing surgery, the expertise of a professor about Canadian history or the expertise of a nurse caring for a psychotic patient. A major problem in Canadian nursing is that there is considerable function overlap between nursing aides, licensed practical nurses, registered psychiatric nurses and registered nurses. These different groups of nurses often have separate legislation and independent regulatory mechanisms. Nursing knowledge is *not* concentrated in the hands of a single group of nursing professionals who are willing to co-operate with each other to achieve goals. Nursing expertise is often viewed by politicians, senior bureaucrats, members of the general public and some nurses as being substitutable in the nursing practice settings. The result is to weaken the control of nursing knowledge and to lessen nursing knowledge and skill as a source of political power. The next item on the agenda for action by nursing leaders is to create an united house in nursing. This is a long-term strategy requiring the most visionary of nursing leaders. The risks are high and the problems many but a successful outcome is crucial.

Mintzberg's theoretical perspectives lead the author to conclude that one of the strongest and most lasting sources of power available to nursing leaders is professional expertise—the knowledge and skill of the individual nurse as she or he gives care at the patient's bedside. Professional expertise takes years to learn and is not easily measurable. The nurse carries this knowledge around in her (his) head, and during the nurse–patient interface puts this body of knowledge and skill to work. Control of this interface belongs to the individual nurse and patient. The work of the expert nurse, like the work of the physician or the university professor is too complex and too exquisite to be controlled by the rules and regulations of a bureaucratic organization. Only the environment surrounding this critical interface is amenable to direct bureaucratic control.

A well developed body of nursing knowledge and skill, that is essential, concentrated and non substitutable, is the most critical source of power that nursing leaders bring to public policy debates. The next item on the agenda for action must be to improve the quality of professional nursing expertise. Nursing knowledge, like medical knowledge, must be grounded in science and nursing practice must be research based. Nurses must have tools of scientific enquiry with which to shape their daily practice. The focus of nursing science must be directed at improving nursing care with a clear benefit to the public.

Political resources

Political scientists refer to the control of resources, a body of knowledge or technical skills as political resources. Political resources, according to Dahl, are anything that can be used 'to sway the specific choices or strategies of another individual'.[18] He stressed that a rich variety of things can provide the basis for political resources and that many participants in the public policy process do not fully exploit their potential resources, resulting in slack in the system. Simeon, in a comprehensive study of the Canadian federal-provincial policy-making process, pointed out that the distribution of political resources varied according to the issue being debated. More importantly, Simeon's research revealed that resources are often not tangible but, rather, subjective depending in a large measure on the beliefs and perceptions of the participants in the public policy process.[19]

Effective participation in the public policy-making process is usually a function of the control of political resources. Studies concerning political participation generally show that individuals and groups possessing large shares of political resources such as income, interest, high socio-economic status, university education, money, legitimacy, commitment, organizational/group cohesiveness, prestige and size, to name a few, tend to participate more frequently in public policy debates than do individuals and groups with fewer resources. This is also the case regarding several other forms of political participation including voting, group membership, active support of political candidates, joining citizen committees, discussing political events and interacting with governmental officials.

The next item on the agenda for action is the identification and use of nursing's political resources, situation by situation. Equally important is the identification of other group leaders' resources and how these will be used.

Certain resources, like higher education, tend to increase the parameters of the individual's interest in and knowledge of the political process as well as contribute to the development of the conceptual skills required for active political involvement. The nursing profession is among the largest and possibly most stable groups in Canada. However, in terms of higher education and occupational status, the nursing profession is grossly disadvantaged if compared to the members of the Canadian Medical Association or to social workers, psychologists, dieticians, physical therapists, occupational therapists or most other health-care professional groups.

Van Loon and Whittington have argued that the size of a group is not by itself a political resource.[20] They suggested that group cohesiveness may be more important. How cohesive is nursing as a group? Do nursing leaders speak for nurses? Would the membership mobilize *en masse* in support of a leader's position? If the answer to the questions is in the affirmative, demands made by the nursing leader in a public policy debate will have increased credibility with governmental decision-makers. Systematic analyses of the nursing profession's political resources have not been reported in the literature but a review of a few of the available studies concerning participation by nurses in various policy issues reveals that the political resources of expertise, time, contacts, money and leadership were significant for success.[21,22]

Dahl has pointed out that the control of political resources is unequally distributed and that various participants differ in their willingness and ability to transform their potential for power into actual power. All public policy debates end up with some people having more power than others.[23] Landes has suggested that this unequal distribution of power exists as long as it is viewed as legitimate by the participants in the public policy process.[24] To what extent is the present distribution of power in the health-care policy fields viewed as legitimate by the various participants? Is the nursing profession's participation in public policy debate viewed as legitimate? by physicians? by the general public? by politicians? by senior bureaucrats? by nurses? If nursing involvement is not viewed as legitimate, the next item on the agenda for action is to devise strategies to change this perception.

The power of legal prerogatives

The fourth general source of power stems from legal prerogatives—the exclusive rights or privileges to impose choice on people and on organizations in the society.[25] This source of power derives from acts of governments and from decisions of the judicial system in the form of regulations, bylaws and judgements. In Canada both nursing professional associations and nursing unions have power which is derived from direct and indirect decisions by governmental decision-makers. Among the most important legal prerogatives that provincial nursing professional associations have in Canada are the right to establish standards for nursing practice and nursing education, the authority to discipline members, the control of the requirements for entry into the profession, and the right to establish requirements for continuing licensure. Nursing professional associations have the legal tools to shape the nursing profession. To exercise this power, the leadership of nursing professional associations must be willing to confront current issues and take visible action.

Simeon has argued that legal authority to function in specific areas is one important reason why the distribution of political resources varies from issue to issue.[26] Legal authority as a source of power has a double-edge since it also provides a constraint on activities of associations and nursing unions. Legal prerogatives grant the right to function in certain areas and not in others.

Nursing unions have the legal prerogatives to bargain with the management of health-care agencies for salary and working conditions, which often include workplace safety, job training and retraining, layoff procedures and job seniority. The ultimate legal prerogative of a union is the right to strike. Most provincial nursing unions have been designated as essential workers and do not have the right to strike. Disputes usually are settled by third party arbitration boards or by governmental decisions. Effective participation by nursing leaders in public policy-making must use legal prerogatives with sensitivity to and firmness in the outcomes as well as the consequences of actions.

The power of access

The fifth general source of power derives simply from having access to people who control the other four sources of powers.[27] Access means having a network of contacts inside governmental agencies, political circles, the nursing profession and in the community at large whose actions and choices the nursing leader seeks to influence. Presthus maintained in his study of the effectiveness of Canadian pressure groups that direct intervention by a leader of an organized group in the formal, political process was a most effective way to influence governmental decisions.[28] Factors, like the prestige and the status of the leader and the group, affect the leader's ability to gain access and establish a network. Van Loon and Whittington argued that governmental decision-makers may be impressed by the leader's ideas and interventions in direct proportion to how impressed they are by the members of the group as individuals.[29]

The most productive points of access at both the provincial and federal levels in Canada tend to be the cabinet and the senior civil service. The factors which are influential with the senior civil servants are, informally, secrecy and expert advice from well-known and credible nursing leaders while the factors that influence politicians are political credibility, past associations and the issues of the moment. Nursing leaders seeking access to senior civil servants and politicians need to tailor their intervention, ideas and approaches to the situation and to the decision-makers whose choices are the focus of the intervention.

The next item on the agenda for action is for nursing organizations to establish a governmental relations office whose purpose would be to maintain a current data base on government agencies, departments and elected officials in terms of departmental activities, key contact people and current issues and concerns from the government's perspective. Having a government relations office is distinct from lobbying. The governmental relations office would provide nursing leaders with current information to be used for effective lobbying. One important access point to the political system is through nurses who hold elected office, and through nurses who are active inside political parties and at senior levels of the bureaucracy. The governmental relations office could help identify and seek advice from these nurses.

The power of access can also be indirect, for example by creating visibility through the use of mass media. A well-known joke in Canada is that Ottawa practises government by the *Globe and Mail*, one of the leading newspapers in the country. The mass media may not be successful in telling citizens what to think, but the media are extremely successful in directing attention to selected topics. The use of the media often encourages governments to deal with issues and problems they would rather ignore. A mass media discussion of nursing issues, which is clearly related to an ongoing debate about health policy, could focus the attention of governmental policy-makers on nursing's concerns and ideas.

Effective communication with the mass media is an acquired skill. Elected politicians learn to respond confidently to the various forms of mass media by consulting communication experts and by trial and error. Nursing leaders must do the same. The importance of learning effective participation skills for involvement in public policy debates must be underscored. This participation includes responding to governmental position papers, writing short features for newspapers as well as letters to editors, returning calls from the media, creating news ideas, sharing information and contacting the media when nursing's viewpoint is ignored.

The power which stems from direct and indirect access is usually based in a relationship of reciprocity and in mutual exchange, not on a dependency relationship. The power of reciprocity stems from favours traded and information shared and often requires giving up power in one situation to gain power in another. The use of this kind of power requires skills in compromise and consensus building. The next item on the agenda for action is in-house training to establish rapport with members of the mass media.

Will, energy and skill

Having a source of power is not enough. Nursing leaders must have the will to use power by expending some time and energy.[30] If the source of power is formal, for example occupying a line management position in a nursing organization, little energy may be required to exercise power. However, power often flows to people who are willing to serve on committees. Sometimes power flows to people with the best information. Sometimes power flows to people who generate new ideas and sometimes power flows to the people who simply out-wait everybody else.

Usually power derived informally (for example from access) requires the expenditure of considerable energy to exercise effectively. Because people who control important sources of power only have so much time and energy, power becomes distributed much more widely than the five sources of power would seem to suggest.[31] This would indicate that nursing leaders would be wise to concentrate time and energy on a few policy areas. What public policy issues are most important to the nursing profession in Canada at the moment? The next item on the agenda for action is to target a few issues and concentrate our sources of power and our time and energy on achieving success in a few highly selected areas. Success with one or two initiatives may have as a consequence an increasing sense of political efficacy among members of the nursing profession. Efficacy is a belief that individuals can influence events by personal effort.[32] Nurses with a high level of political efficacy believe the governmental decision-makers will pay attention to their efforts and are more likely to be active participants in the public policy process.

Having some source of power, and expending time and energy, may come to naught unless the nursing leader proceeds with political skill. Political skill in this sense means the ability to use the source of power effectively—to persuade others, to use expertise and information to the fullest ·in bargaining, to exercise authority with sensitivity to others, to know where and when to concentrate efforts, to sense what is possible, to mobilize followers and create the necessary alliances and to devise winning strategies.[15]

Related to political skills are a set of intrinsic leadership characteristics: charisma, verbal ability and attractiveness.[16] Skilful use of these suggests that the package has some influence on the impact of the message.

Viewing power and using Henry Mintzberg's theoretical perspective, lead rapidly to the conclusion that both men and women have the potential for power: that power is not distributed evenly in public policy debates; that power is not democratic; that it is not fair; and that power unused, evaporates. That nurses and their leaders have varying degrees of power depending on their sources of power, the available time, will and energy and their political and leadership skills. That power and political resources are rooted in the social context, the issue of the moment and, perhaps most significantly, in the perceptions of the participants in the debates.

Summary

In this chapter, the author has argued that nursing leaders must increasingly become involved in the rough and tumble of public policy debates in a few selected fields, for example in health care and higher education. Participation in public policy-making means involvement in the process of allocating the scarce resources of Canadian society. To be effective, Canadian nursing leaders need to use their sources of power and influence for political purposes. The author has further argued that the nursing profession's most lasting source of power is the professional expertise of individual staff nurses as they give nursing care at the patient's bedside. Finally, an agenda for action is outlined.

References

1. Lasswell, H. D., *Politics: Who Gets What, When and How*. McGraw-Hill, New York, 1936.

2. Dye, T., *Policy Analysis: What Governments Do, Why They Do It and What Difference it Makes.* The University of Alabama Press, University, Alabama, 1976, p. 1.
3. Doern, G. B. and Phidd, R. W., *Canadian Public Policy: Ideas, Structure, Process.* Methuen, Toronto, 1983, p. 34.
4. See reference 3, p. 34.
5. See reference 3, p. 43.
6. See reference 3, p. 34.
7. See reference 3, p. 51.
8. See reference 3, p. 51.
9. Adapted from reference 3, p. 54.
10. See reference 3, p. 57.
11. See reference 3, pp. 58–59.
12. Mintzberg, H., *Power in and Around Organizations.* Prentice-Hall, Englewood Cliffs, NJ, 1983, p. 23.
13. See reference 12, p. 5.
14. Raven, B. H. and Kruglanski, M. C., 'Conflict and power' in Swingle, P. G. (ed.), *The Structure of Conflict.* Academic Press, New York, 1975, pp. 177–219.
15. See reference 12, p. 24.
16. See reference 12, p. 24.
17. See reference 12, p. 24.
18. Dahl, Robert A., *Who Governs? Democracy and Power in the American City.* Prentice-Hall, New Haven, 1961, p. 226.
19. Simeon, Richard, *Federal-Provincial Diplomacy.* University of Toronto Press, Toronto, 1972, p. 201.
20. Van Loon, Richard J. and Whittington, Michael S., *The Canadian Political System.* McGraw-Hill Ryerson, Toronto, 1976, p. 303.
21. Oakley, Deborah and Sochalski, Julie, *Michigan Nurse*, 1986, **59**(9) 3–4.
22. Archer, Sarah E., 'A study of nurse administrators' political participation', *Western Journal of Nursing Research*, 1983, **5**(1), 65–75.
23. See reference 18, p. 17.
24. Landes, Ronald G., *The Canadian Policy.* Prentice-Hall, Scarborough, Ontario, 1983, p. 47.
25. See reference 12, p. 24.
26. See reference 19, p. 202.
27. See reference 12, p. 24.
28. Presthus, Robert, *Elite Accommodation in Canadian Politics.* Macmillan, Toronto, 1973, p. 123.
29. See reference 20, p. 303.
30. See reference 12, p. 25.
31. See reference 12, p. 25.
32. See reference 28, p. 123.
33. See reference 12, p. 25.

Political Issues in Nursing: Past, Present and Future, Volume 3
Edited by R. White
© 1988 John Wiley & Sons Ltd

CHAPTER 2

The influence of nursing on the politics of health

ROSEMARY WHITE, SRN, SCM, OHNC, MSc, PhD
Independent researcher and writer on the history of nursing, East Stratton, Winchester, Hants, England

Most nursing journals these days seem to include at least one reference to the politics of health, nursing's need to become more politically minded or how well nurses are doing in lobbying in the halls of policy-making. Nurses have been persuaded over the past few years to become more politically minded and to take a more active part in the politics of nursing and health care.

It may be true that most nurses have begun to differentiate between party politics and the negotiations and bargaining that precede policy-making. It is less clear, though, that nurses have much understanding of the process of policy-making or of how policy-making institutions work. On the whole, they have relied on their nursing institutions to represent them in these issues and to select policies on their behalf, and seem content to follow their leaders without much discrimination.

There are, however, those nurses who prefer to think for themselves and who do not invariably believe in the policies put forward by their institutions or their leaders. There is evidence[1] that these nurses are beginning to develop their own philosophies of nursing and policies for health care. These nurses, slowly organizing themselves into more articulate groups, may soon prefer to seek to influence health care on lines that differ from those pursued by their more bureaucratically minded colleagues.

Health-care systems have become bureaucratic and suffer from all the rigidity and characteristics of bureaucracies. They are hierarchical, inflexible and impersonal. They respond to policies determined by the government or Big Business.[2] They are organized to give care to the mass of people on the most efficient lines and within budgetary constraints fixed by distant managers. They are slow to respond to changes in society, do little to develop or motivate their staff and, generally, cannot respond to personal needs of the individual.

As Robinson and Strong[3] point out, efficiency is not the same as effectiveness and as I have previously shown, managerial values and objectives are not always the same as those of the professionally minded nurses.[1,4,5]

In order for nurses to be effective in influencing health-care and nursing policies, there is a need for them to understand the system. Most nurses do not have this understanding. In the past we have had many opportunities to make changes which would have developed the effectiveness and professional status of nurses but these have been dissipated in the search for other goals.[6] Nurses do not receive training in policy-making and have often failed to perceive their opportunities.

At the start of the National Health Service, in 1948, the government attempted to establish locally based joint consultative committees (JCCs) in the hospital groups, to provide a means of consultation between staff and management. The Royal College of Nursing (RCN) tried to prevent student nurses from taking part in these in order to safeguard their student status and in the ensuing confusion the College withdrew its support of the scheme, which eventually collapsed.[6] The doctors also decided not to take part in the JCCs but set up their own consultative committees which became very powerful components of the local policy-making machinery.

In 1974, the DHSS sought to set up professional advisory committees to offer advice to the newly reorganized NHS. Nursing and Midwifery Professional Advisory Committees (NMPACs) were established under a model constitution which allowed different sections of nurses to elect their own representatives and, also, a small number of nurses to be co-opted.[3] Once again, the nurses failed to perceive the opportunities that the NMPACs offered them to shape policy-making. Furthermore, senior nurses saw these committees as either intruding on their authority or as something to be manipulated by means of the co-opted members and the agenda. In any event, the NMPACs proved to be of little value either to the health authorities or to the nurses themselves. Certainly they failed to match the influence of the medical advisory committees and there was little of any value in what advice the nurses managed to give.

There is, then, a considerable element of innocence amongst nurses who seek to influence policy-making. They are ignorant of the machinery of their health authorities, of their nursing institutions and of government. Worse still, too many are innocent of how they are manipulated for political reasons by their nurse managers, their leaders and their representative unions or associations. They either expect too little or too much. This chapter seeks to clarify to some modest extent the routes, problems and constraints of policy-making. I have drawn very largely from my own studies of British nursing but, of course, these are not enough to allow me to generalize on an international basis. I am indebted, therefore, to the many contributors to this series of *Political Issues in Nursing: Past, Present and Future*. From collaborators, as well as from other students, I have been able to learn much of their concerns and difficulties in other parts of the developed world.

The chapter will be roughly divided into four main themes:

(1) the failure of nursing influence in the politics of health;
(2) how policies are made;
(3) constraints on policy-making in nursing;
(4) how nurses can be more influential in policy-making.

If some of this appears to ring rather pessimistically, I hope that the conclusion of the chapter will leave a more optimistic note.

The failure of nursing influence on the politics of health

Nursing is frequently regarded as a marginal occupation which has, or should have, little concern with the politics of health. Nurses are there to *do*, not to think. We are still often thought of as being the tools by which many policies are implemented rather than the makers or partners in the making of policy.

As a historian I can say that in many ways this view is correct but that in other respects it is inaccurate. The trouble is that, on the whole, nurses have had little manifest power in the past, have not known how to use what power they had, and so have learned to prefer an oblique approach rather than to become embroiled in a frontal attack. We tend to go around, or surmount, difficulties rather than to confront them. We are better at reacting than proacting. We make the most of a situation rather than seeking to establish the optimum conditions. And, on the whole, we are not very brave at confronting reality. However, this is changing and in one country after another, nurses are now seeking to have greater influence in the politics of health.

Nurses have traditionally been characterized by altruism, and continue to be so. Politicians have found this element of our profession convenient to keep us out of major policy-making as well as to maintain low levels of pay and, on the whole, poor working conditions. While the doctors have been able to demand high rates of remuneration and the best equipment, nurses have had to make do with poor salaries and the minimum of equipment. Our spirit of altruism and our willingness to put the patient first have ensured that we make do with few tools in our technical work and that we take over the work of domestic, clerical, administrative and technical workers when they finish their work after 5.00 pm and at week-ends.

However, in recent years, nurses have begun to understand that altruism is not a sufficient foundation for establishing or maintaining a good health service.[4] It is neither sufficient for our patients or clients, nor is it a strong enough basis for establishing the professionalism of nursing or for influencing the politics of health.

For many years we have asserted that there is a unique component to nursing which neither medics nor untrained staff are able to supply. Challenged to describe this unique element of our work we were unable to isolate it until Henderson[7] identified it in her analysis of the nursing function. This description of our responsibility was the key to our cognitive understanding and opened out further analysis of the knowledge and skills which were required from professional nurses. It clarified for us the theoretical areas which underpin our function and should shape our training and policy-making.

The profession of nursing covers a wide range of roles from political leader, nurse manager or administrator, through teacher and guide to patients, doctors, students and colleagues, to technician and bedside carer. There have been many attempts to identify the role of the nurse, all of which have been only partially successful. Indeed, Anderson[8] found that, at one and the same time, different people have different understandings of our roles which may change from moment to moment as the situation demands. Too often we have allowed others to dictate our role rather than determining it for ourselves.

Nursing has also been characterized as a unitary occupation with a unity of goals and needs, a single value system and a consensus on strategy. My own research[6] has shown this not to be so. I have found that nursing is a plural society with three distinguishable subgroups. In the first place, there are the 'managers' whose primary need is to control their nursing staff, to maintain nursing cover within the constraints of their budgets and to uphold the status quo which, in turn, supports their authority within the power structure of the health-care system. In the second place, there are the 'generalists' who are in nursing as a job in order to earn a living. The sociologists describe these people as 'functionalists' whose primary concern is to maximize their material rewards and conditions of work. They gain satisfaction from their work but are not so much concerned to earn professional authority or further their knowledge base as they are intent on maintaining their functional position in the hierarchy. In the division of labour, the generalists are the task workers and are content to work within the hierarchy, supervised by the nurse managers. They are, therefore, also satisfied by the preservation of the status quo and are inclined to be more unionistic in their strategies.

The third group of nurses are the professionally minded. The sociologists call these the 'specialists' since they tend to look for professional authority based on higher education and a specialized knowledge base. These professionalists seek to control the whole process of nursing and may often supervise the work of the task workers or generalists. Because their authority is based on further training and a specialized knowledge base, they tend to challenge the status quo and the vertical power structure of nursing. Therefore there is often conflict between these professionalists and the nurse managers and generalists.

In describing these three groups of nurses, I am describing groups of people with different goals, needs, strategies and value systems. I am not trying to maintain that all nurse managers employ bureaucratic values since there are some who are professionally minded. However, peer group pressures are strong and it is often very difficult for a superintendent nurse or hospital matron to establish her position with her peers, who are the lay administrators and treasurers, unless she adopts their criteria.[1] Similarly, it may happen that a graduate nurse may prefer the values of the generalists.

In seeking to determine policies for the nursing society, therefore, it will often happen that a decision that is deemed to be for the good of the profession may favour one or two of these groups but be antithetical to the needs of the third group.

Since nursing is so firmly regarded as a unitary society, all our institutions are structured and geared to cater for a unitary body. There is, therefore, an insistence on consensus which is not available. In the past, because professionalist nurses have been rather thin on the ground, their voice has been suppressed and, too often, disregarded. More recently, all over the world, the numbers of professionally minded nurses have increased and their voices are becoming more insistent and better organized. Everywhere, the nursing institutions are becoming aware that the unity of nursing is beginning to show cracks and that nursing associations are experiencing more and more difficulty in representing both their unionistic and their professionally minded members.[5,9,10] For reasons which I shall explain later, the nursing associations have had to adopt what is known in policy-making as the 'common good'. That is to say, they have had to align themselves with many of the values determined by the civil service or policy-makers of their countries. Therefore, the associations' strategies have become more closely akin to those of the nurse managers. Since the generalists also favour the status quo, they can more easily fall into line. The unitary ideology of nursing favours the recruitment of more and more nurses and the institutions are geared to negotiating for pay and working conditions rather than to professional authority or standards of care.

In Britain, the principal association representing nurses, the RCN, has a majority membership of generalist nurses with a declining educational entry level[6] and has become dependent on their numbers for its power. In the US, the American Nursing Association (ANA) has become locked into a situation where it has to support the diploma nurse in the face of mounting demands from nurse practitioners and more highly qualified nurses.[9] In Canada, the Canadian Nurses Association has found itself in a situation where it is supporting administrative systems which act against the professional standards of its nurses and which are helping to proletarianize its members.[11] Therefore the traditional nursing associations are able to recruit generalist members and to satisfy them and the managers while the professionalists find themselves out in the cold. These nurses are, therefore, seeking to set up their own associations, the better to represent their interests.

How are policies made?

It will be helpful here briefly to review some aspects of policy-making. Hall, Land, Parker and Webb[12] have given an excellent account of policy-making and it is convenient to draw from their analysis.

They see policy-making partly as a process of demands and supports: 'demands are directed towards the authorities of a political system who are being pressed, encouraged or persuaded to make certain kinds of decisions, and take certain actions'. There are bound to be a number and variety of demands and these, therefore, need to be regulated or combined—and so modified. In a democratic process the authorities have to satisfy their supporters if they are to continue to maintain their authority. A certain number of demands must therefore be conceded, but the choice of demands on which the authorities will act will depend on the type of support available and every decision made has a cost. Sometimes there are long-term benefits with short-term costs but, more commonly, there are short-term benefits with long-term costs and, of course, support for an authority may be volatile.

In order to maximize its support, the authority needs to gain general acceptance of its regime and one way of doing this is to foster a belief in the existence of a national or a common interest. If the authorities can be seen to be guardians of the public good, sectional interests can be more easily subordinated to it. This concept of the 'common good' allows the ruling authorities to attract support as the body which is best placed to make judgements about the general interest, and strengthens their ability to influence factional interests by suggesting that the common good lies in compromise or deferral of certain demands.

The issue of the common good can also be used by interest groups to influence the ruling authority *and their own members*. The interest group's ability to influence government is determined by the way in which it puts forward its demands as well as the number and prestige of its members. Demands will come from a number of interest groups and have, therefore, to be regulated. This is achieved by the structure of the political system and by the nature of norms and values.

Structural regulation is effected by the interest groups themselves who have to act as gatekeepers by assessing their own priorities. If the interest groups put forward every demand without due consideration, this would rapidly destroy their credibility and influence with the ruling authority. They therefore have to be selective and are always constrained by their degree of specialized knowledge. The interest groups are also constrained by the support they can muster from their own members.

Current norms and values are no less powerful in determining what demands may be put forward. These often decide the nature of the common good as well as the choice and timing of demands. There is often a general agreement of current norms and values but, frequently, they are specific to each interest group. Changes in the political or economic climate may sometimes effect a shift in these norms or values. There is, however, in all political systems, a strong preference for stability and the maintenance of the status quo which acts to resist change, regulate demands and preserve support for the prevailing authority leadership and the generalized common good, thus regulating political conflict. In regard to policy decisions for nursing, it is clear that the institutions act as the voice of their members and that they also act as the gatekeepers.

In the past, nursing has lacked a scientific base for practice. While this may be changing now, the accumulation of a knowledge base is still very slow and most nursing practice continues to be grounded in historical (some would say mythological) precedent. In the search for an economic base for establishing staffing and skill-mix ratios, research resources have been expended on dependency studies which, in turn, have been employed with managerial values rather than in the search for higher standards of care.[13] Where there is a scientific base for certain clinical procedures, this is often ignored or misunderstood in practice by the generalists who are not predisposed to use the best available knowledge without adequate leadership.

Demands for decisions or action may be made by individuals or subgroups in the association but they are filtered by the leadership. In this filtering process, the nurse leaders will employ their own norms and values and will have their own understanding of the common good within nursing.[5] There is, therefore, more chance that demands relating to the management of the nursing service or to the interests of the generalists will pass through these gatekeepers than will those of the professionalists. And since policies relating to the bureaucratic or fiscal management of the service are nearer the priorities of the government, it is these that are more likely to receive attention than those relating to quality of care or the development of a professionalist element in nursing.

Constraints on policy-making in nursing

Before the nursing associations can be accepted by government departments as partners in policy-making, they have to fulfil certain criteria. Nettl and Eckstein have each examined these qualifications for interest groups. Nettl[14] found that the ethos of decision-making, at least in Britain, is set by the attitudes, values and procedures current in the civil service and that it is the civil service which defines what is the common good. In order to be admitted as a partner in policy-making, associations have to adopt the methods, language and attitudes of the civil servants. Thus, leaders of an association seeking to influence policy have to become part of a consensus: effectively, they eventually cease to be leaders of their association and become civil servants with an interest in their associations.

Eckstein[15] found that pressure groups tend to deal with the more powerful elements of a government department rather than with the formal structure. Thus, if the nursing division in the health department is weak in power, the nursing associations will prefer to by-pass it and establish links with the medical division or lay administrators. He also found that there is an interplay between the structure, activities and attitudes of the government department and the pressure group and that the pressure group will restructure itself to resemble the department it is seeking to influence. In other words, the association will tend to mirror the government department by establishing a bureaucracy of its own. Eckstein also described how a two-way influence is achieved more by day-to-day informal contacts between officials than by public campaigns. The leaders of interest groups, therefore, tend to guard their relationships with the government policy-makers, often to the detriment of their relationships with their members.

Interest groups must be seen to be representative of the majority of their members and must have the power to commit those whom they represent. There should be one organization speaking for most members rather than several competing organizations, unable to muster a sizeable majority. Hence the preference by nursing organizations for unity in nursing. The most powerful groups are those with *specialized technical knowledge* and competence relating to the policies and administrative forms that impinge on their own fields of practice. Their members are more usually in influential positions and the group enjoys public prestige and support. Since the professionalists in nursing have been marginalized, our leaders are more often drawn from the nurse managers who are in top bureaucratic posts and are more visible but who also employ their managerial values in interpreting nursing needs. From these criteria it may be seen that nursing enjoys certain benefits but also experiences certain disadvantages.

Since nursing has traditionally been regarded as a unitary profession, the majority of whose members are generalists and task workers, this will be the generalized image given to it. The public and the civil servants will conjure up a picture of the little angel smoothing a patient's brow and will not consider the technical competence and cognitive skills possessed by the minority of professionalists. Even in the United States, where there is the largest proportion of graduate nurses, the picture portrayed in books, films and on the television screen is of the diploma nurse, or practical nurse, rather than the specialist practitioner. Officially, then, nurses are not usually regarded as having a legitimate knowledge base and are often seen as semi-skilled workers.

The bulk of nurses are also women and nursing, therefore, suffers from all the deprivations of a female occupation. Furthermore, the numbers of nurses are large and the cost of a nursing service in any health service forms the largest single salary bill. Similarly, the bill for training this large population of nurses is high, especially as most countries seek to train their nurses to a common first level.

It is therefore logistically and economically difficult for any nursing service to insist on training all its nurses to a legitimate, professional level, sufficient to gain political advantage in policy-making. In Britain, we have in the past been forced to rely on influence gained from numerical strength rather than from technical and specialized knowledge.

In seeking to be recognized as partners in policy-making, we have had to recruit as many members as possible to our nursing organizations, including our enrolled nurses. In the US and Canada, the nursing associations have had a similar experience as Fondiller[9] and Baumgart[10] have described. This has tended to reinforce the public image of nursing and existing attitudes.

In order to be legitimized as policy-makers, our associations have also had to show themselves to be responsible and to support the common good by assisting in the recruitment of more nurses rather than better recruits. In Britain this means that the minimum entry qualification for candidates for nurse training has been depressed rather than raised. Our associations have become bureaucratized and are sometimes in danger of being out of touch with their members. In seeking to represent the bulk of their members, the voice of the minority is not heard. In trying to maintain the ideology of a unitary occupation, latent groups and new ideas are suppressed.

With a large membership, the association has to act as a referee and find a balance between the interests of the subgroups within it. At the same time, it tries to demonstrate to the outside world the strength of consensus and harmony in its decision-making. Thus, by a policy of unity, the nursing associations fail to recognize the subgroups who might act as a countervailing force to the prevailing power structure. As I have said, this policy is beginning to show important cracks.

What can nurses do to be more influential?

There is a common recognition that nursing, with its extensive range of functions and roles, needs a wide field of recruitment. Since the Second World War, every investigation and report into British nursing has put forward proposals for recruits to be drawn from those people with the minimum of formal educational qualifications to those with a university degree. Every report has proposed that there should be some form of nursing team with members having a basic preparation and the team leaders having an advanced preparation. However, it is interesting to note that this common understanding of the need for a wide field of recruitment was, in general, expressed in two models with a critical difference. During the periods when there was a conservative government in power, the reports proposed different routes and standards of entry for the basic nurses and the advanced nurses. The Horder Report[16] described this model as having 'officers' to lead the team and 'other ranks' to be the labour force. After the war years, when there was a greater disposition towards egalitarianism and socialism, the reports proposed a single avenue of recruitment for all grades and levels of nurse preparation. Other countries, such as Canada and the US, have also found that they need to employ well-trained nursing staff supported by a team of staff with more basic preparation. In the North American continent, they have been trying to move towards an all-graduate level of nurses but the logistics and costs of this policy have so far prevented its full implementation.

The Horder model is comparable with other public services throughout the world. If we look at the armed services, the police forces and the civil services we should find that in each service there are officers and other ranks. In most countries there is one policy of recruitment, training and salary structure for the officers or specialists and different policy structures for the other ranks. Since this is the case for these public services, we should ask why it is not so for nurses, and why all nurses should have to pass through the ranks before promotion to the officer levels. My guess is that nursing has, traditionally, sought to copy the medical profession in which all members are professionalists, and that the nursing associations have evolved around their policy of unity, have found their strength in numbers rather than specialized knowledge and are now in a position where they would find it very difficult indeed to change.

If the association sought to achieve the two-level model put forward by Horder, with accelerated promotion for the 'officer' class, it would lose the support of its generalist members. On the other hand, if the association continues to support the generalists, it will lose the support of its professionalist members, a small minority. There is, therefore, considerable pressure for the association to seek to maintain the status quo even if this means raising the educational preparation for *all* nurses while retaining the common first level of qualification. We see this phenomenon in Britain today[17] even though historical and current evidence shows that it is a logistically and economically unfeasible policy which will, eventually, incur compromise and incoherence. While the styles of the status quo in the US and Canada are different, the pressures to retain it remain as strong.

Socialized as nurses are in the ethic of unity, they have come to fear conflict. Dissenting voices are labelled by their associations as rebels and are accused of disloyalty. This process does not dispel conflict: it only smothers it. Hall, Land, Parker and Webb[12] have suggested that policy-making is either a plural or an elitist process. With an ideology of unity, there is always a danger of an oligarchy or of being dominated by a ruling elite which tends to foster the status quo and inhibit change. On the other hand, a model of pluralism would disperse power and produce better opportunities for change and flexibility.

We must learn that conflict is not a negative or destructive force. The ideology of service and altruism persists among all nurses and constitutes a very strong occupational culture which helps to maintain a common core to nursing and holds together all the various groups. The differences between the groups tend to separate them and there is continuing conflict between them. The cultural cohesion of nurses, and the conflict between them, together form a tension which is constructive and healthy. A policy of unity and consensus leads to a preservation of the status quo, the suppression both of movement and of the emergence of new ideas and groups. This is destructive of any organization and ensures the alienation of minorities as we have found in Britain, the US and Canada. A tension, as I have described, permits growth and change. It allows new ideas and new groups to emerge. In a healthy pluralist society there should always be a tension between the prevailing and countervailing groups. It may be that this balance of interests shifts from time to time as the economic or political climate changes or as attitudes and values shift.

The term 'conflict' has two meanings: one is opposition or division of interest and the other involves a Marxian struggle between individuals or groups. These two meanings need to be distinguished from each other since the former includes concepts of interdependence, a concourse of divided interests and some sort of harmonious equilibrium, whereas the second meaning involves an atomized society with aggregates of groups pursuing their own interests.

Certain conflicts can only be possible because of shared convictions, and conflict and consensus need not be mutually exclusive. We see examples of this phenomenon in religion where there is consensus of conviction but a conflict of interpretation. Conflict, meaning a concourse of divided interests, is a feature of a mature and developed society and nursing must aim to achieve this.

We should also remember the question of norms, attitudes and timing in framing policies for health care. In an earlier part of this chapter I suggested that nursing has been regarded as a marginal occupation, subordinate to medicine in the health-care systems. It is not usually treated as a public service comparable to the armed services or civil service. I believe that this is changing. It is noticeable that in the developing countries, especially in Africa where they have had to construct policies for the establishment of a new system, less emphasis is placed on hospitals and considerable emphasis is lodged on community care. In the Western world of developed countries, there is now a much wider understanding of the nature of health. Other factors can also be taken into account such as the growing costs of health care, the expanding role of the clinical nurse, the changing nature of morbidity and mortality, the aging population and the greater incidence of irreversible illnesses.

Seedhouse[18] has explored the conventional theories of health (including the WHO definition) and has grouped them into four:

(1) that health is an ideal state;
(2) that health is the physical and mental state to perform socialized daily duties;
(3) that health is a commodity;
(4) that health is a personal strength or ability.

He found that each of these theories had strengths and weaknesses and has proposed that different professions or groups of people will prefer one or other of the theories. As an all-inclusive concept of health, Seedhouse has offered the theory that:

a person's optimum health is equivalent to the state of the set of conditions which fulfill or enable a person to work to fulfill his or her realistic, chosen and biological potentials. Some of these conditions are of the highest importance for all people. Others are variable dependent upon individual abilities and circumstances.

He suggests therefore that the health worker needs to work to remove obstacles to the achievement of human potential, whether these obstacles are biological, environmental, psychological, political, social, institutional or otherwise. In other words, he sees health as a very individual and personal state and the health worker as one who builds foundations for the individual who must be allowed to be the designer or architect of his own destiny, to exert his own autonomy.

If we accept Seedhouse's concept of health, or even if we only accept some parts of the four groups of health theories that he has delineated, any health policies that are put forward must be very broadly based and not be restricted to the care of physically or mentally ill people or concerned only with conventional nursing.

The expanding role of the nurse must be distinguished from the extending role. I understand the use of the extending role to mean that the nurse receives more tasks delegated to her by the medics: these are usually of a technical nature and she performs them by agreement with a specific doctor. In an expanding role the nurse will follow her usual role (defined by Henderson)[7] at a broader and deeper level. Thus her perception of the client's needs and problems will be more pervasive and encompassing than previously and her armamentarium of solutions or her avenues of provision will similarly be more sensitive to his personal design or autonomy.

The growing cost of health care has provoked a greater interest in community care and a search for less expensive methods of administering the system. Clearly, both these factors, together with the expanding role of the nurse, will encourage the authorities to look to nursing for a greater input.

Demographic changes in our populations mean that in many developed countries there are now more old people to look after. Modern medicine has allowed more people with chronic illnesses or disabilities to survive. Recent shifts in morbidity patterns, including cancer, the diseases of affluence or behaviour and new diseases such as Legionnaires' disease, hepatitis-B, auto-immune deficiency disease and other viral infections for which we have as yet no cure, all mean that nursing must take the brunt of care for these people. The hospice movement relies heavily on good and knowledgeable nursing. A similar pattern of care for AIDs victims is already being developed. These new institutions make great demands on the understanding and skills of nurses and will, increasingly, require more nurses of a high calibre. In the US and Canada the system of nurse practitioners has developed. In England, within the National Health Service, we are developing nursing homes for the frail and elderly in which the nurses take complete charge of all inhabitants without medical supervision. It appears therefore that nursing will once again come to the fore of health-care systems and that, prompted by economic needs, attitudes towards nurses may change in our favour.

We can use these opportunities to influence health-care policy. If we learn to understand our own nursing institutions, how they function, their constraints and their strengths, if we watch the changing nature of the common good, the shifting political and economic climate, and if we perceive and understand the emerging patterns of need, we shall be able to increase our influence. We must use the moment to develop and improve the training and education of our 'officer' leaders, to give them a satisfactory clinical career structure, to continue to develop our research and our specialized knowledge base. We must ensure that the voice of the professionalist minority has a hearing and is heeded. For it is only by doing all these things that we shall be able to continue to recruit enough 'other ranks' of good quality. We need all grades of nurses but if we alienate the professionalists and drive them from nursing, the rest of our nurses will suffer and there will be a continuing decline in numbers, quality and influence.

We should seek to achieve an image of nursing as a public service and, in doing this, we must ensure that we establish an elite of clinical specialists and other leaders. In other public services it would be unthinkable to recruit our colonels, naval commanders, police commissioners and civil service leaders only from those who had entered through the ranks. In most democratic countries there are separate avenues for the recruitment and training of these officers and technical specialists, an accelerated form of promotion for them and different structures for their salary negotiations. This does not preclude the promotion of able candidates from the ranks but it does avoid the random form of leadership ladder for nurses that Hardy[19] has described. With a separate entry and qualification system for nursing leaders and officers, we should be able to impart values and attitudes to them which are strong enough to favour professional goals rather than bureaucratic ones. We should be able to develop a leadership that is young enough and flexible enough to react, or proact, to changing social trends and needs and, thus, to shape appropriate policies in health care in good time.

We must nurture the professionalist element in nursing and guard it from the bureaucratization that has overtaken our generalist and manager colleagues. With their capacity to conceptualize and analyse, it will be the professionalists who will be able to identify needs, formulate policies and shape their implementation. It will also be, as it has been recently, the academic nurses who analyse the outcomes of policies. We should always remember that many policies in the past have been 'symbolic policies'[20] and that the implementation of policies often suffers from 'policy drift'.[20] All policies should be monitored and their outcomes analysed[21] to ensure that we go where we mean to go.

Just as society has become more complex, policy-making is becoming more complex. If nursing is to be an influence to the good for health care, we need to ensure that there are nurses who are adequately trained and prepared and whose values never let them forget that politics is people and that people need good nurses.

References

1. White, Rosemary, 'Pluralism, professionalism and politics in nursing', *International Journal of Nursing Studies*, 1983, **2**, no. 4, 231–244.
2. Milio, Nancy, 'Nursing within the ecology of public health: a case in point'. In White, Rosemary (ed.), *Political Issues in Nursing: Past, Present and Future*. John Wiley, Chichester, 1985, vol. 1, Chapter 5.
3. Robinson, Jane and Strong, Philip, 'Professional nursing advice: an interim report', Nursing Policy Studies 1, Nursing Policy Study Group, University of Warwick, 1987.
4. White, Rosemary, 'Altruism is not enough: some barriers in the development of nursing as a profession', *Journal of Advanced Nursing*, 1984, **9**, 505–512.
5. White, Rosemary, 'From matron to manager: the political construction of reality'. In White, Rosemary, (ed.), *Political Issues in Nursing: Past, Present and Future*. John Wiley, Chichester, 1986, vol. 2, Chapter 3.
6. White, Rosemary, *The Effects of the NHS on the Nursing Profession: 1948–1961*. King's Fund Historical Series 3, King Edward's Hospital Fund for London, 1985, distributed by Oxford University Press.
7. Henderson, Virginia, 'The basic principles of nursing', *Nursing Mirror* Reprint, 1958.
8. Anderson, Evelyn R., *The Role of the Nurse*, the Study of Nursing Care Project, 1973, Series 2, no. 1, RCN, London.
9. Fondiller, Shirley H., 'The American Nurses Association and National League for Nursing: political relationships and realities'. In White, Rosemary (ed.), *Political Issues in Nursing: Past, Present and Future*. John Wiley, Chichester, 1986, vol. 2, Chapter 7.
10. Baumgart, Alice, 'The conflicting demands of professionalism and trade unionism', *International Nursing Review*, 1983, **30**, no. 5, 150–155.

11. See Chapter 4, Campbell, Marie L. and Chapter 3, Storch, Janet L. and Stinson, Shirley, M., this volume.
12. Hall, Phoebe, Land, Hilary, Parker, Roy and Webb, Adrian, *Change, Choice and Conflict*. Heinemann, London, 1975.
13. See Chapter 4, Campbell, Marie L. See also Chapter 5, this volume. MacGuire, Jillian M. for a contrasting view.
14. Nettl, J. P., 'Consensus or elite domination: the case of business'. In Castles, F. G., Murray, D. J. and Potter, D. C. (eds), *Decisions, Organisations and Society*. Penguin, Harmondsworth, 1971, Chapter 14.
15. Eckstein, H., 'The determinants of pressure group politics'. In Castles, F. G., Murray, D. J. and Potter, D. C. (eds), *Decisions, Organisations and Society*. Penguin, Harmondsworth, 1971, Chapter 11.
16. Royal College of Nursing Reconstruction Committee, Reports 1942–1949, RCN, London.
17. United Kingdom Central Council for Nursing, Midwifery and Health Visiting, 'Project 2000: a new preparation for practice', UKCC, London, 1986.
18. Seedhouse, David, *Health: the Foundations for Achievement*. John Wiley, Chichester, 1986.
19. Hardy, Leslie K., 'Career politics: the case of career histories of selected leading female and male nurses in England and Scotland'. In White, Rosemary (ed.), *Political Issues in Nursing: Past, Present and Future*. John Wiley, Chichester, 1986, vol. 2, Chapter 4.
20. McIntosh, Jean B., 'District nursing: a case of political marginality'. In White, Rosemary (ed.), *Political Issues in Nursing: Past, Present and Future*. John Wiley, Chichester, 1985, vol. 1, Chapter 3.
21. White, Rosemary, 'Policy implications and constraints in the role of the nurse in the management of pain'. In Copp, Laurel (ed.), *Perspectives on Pain*. Churchill Livingstone, Edinburgh, 1985, Chapter 6.

Political Issues in Nursing: Past, Present and Future, Volume 3
Edited by R. White
© 1988 John Wiley & Sons Ltd

CHAPTER 3

Concepts of deprofessionalization with applications to nursing

JANET L. STORCH, RN, MHSA, PhD
Associate Professor, Department of Health Services Administration and Community Medicine and Associate Professor, Faculty of Nursing
and
SHIRLEY M. STINSON, RN, EdD, LLD
Professor and Associate Dean, Faculty of Nursing, and Professor, Department of Health Services Administration and Community Medicine

University of Alberta, Edmonton, Alberta, Canada

Introduction

During the decades of the 1950s and 1960s, the professionalization of occupations seemed to be on the rise in Western industrialized nations, as indicated by the growing numbers of occupational groups seeking to be recognized as professions.[1,2] Many observers saw this rise as a positive force in social development and envisioned a professionalized future as a desirable future[3,4] on the premise that the pursuit of the two distinguishing characteristics of a professional group, the 'basic body of abstract knowledge and the ideal of service',[5] was a process beneficial to society as a whole.

Those who did not share this view became more vocal in the 1970s. Some of these observers suggested that professions were, in fact, powerful, monopolistic oligarchies and should be recognized as such.[6,7] Others claimed that the nature of the professions was changing and described this change from various theoretical perspectives.[8,9]

It is apparent that nursing, as an occupational group, is not immune to these various assessments and these changes, and that over time there has been both movement towards greater professionalism and movement away from this goal. In order to understand the nature, processes and consequences of these changes, it is important to appreciate the different perspectives from which these changes might be viewed, since different perspectives will lead to different conclusions about the effects of these changes and their significance. It is the purpose of this chapter to critically assess the literature on deprofessionalization, identifying the various concepts of change, and to discuss some applications of these changes to nursing.

Concepts of change: the literature

The steadily growing amount of literature on deprofessionalization is found in professional journals, sociological journals, books and in a dissertation. In most cases, the writers adopt the public image of the profession based on the classic, older professions such as medicine, the law and the clergy. The assumption underlying the discussion with reference to a specific occupational group is that professionalism had once existed for that group. In reviewing this literature it is apparent that at least three types of change are being discussed under the umbrella of deprofessionalization, including (1) deprofessionalization as deskilling, (2) deprofessionalization as proletarianization, and (3) deprofessionalization as an erosion of professional knowledge and trust.

Deprofessionalization as deskilling

The bulk of literature on deprofessionalization specific to a particular type of occupational grouping centres on mental health professionals, which include psychiatrists, clinical psychologists, psychiatric social workers and psychiatric nurses. In many cases, deprofessionalization is linked to the development of community mental health centres and the resulting confusion between the role of these centres and the delivery modes of traditional mental health services.[10,11] Deprofessionalization in this case involves a 'gradual movement away from the use of professionals in both administration of the Centres and direct treatment of patients'.[12]

But, according to other authors, the deprofessionalization of psychiatry is not restricted to the mental health centres but is occurring in mental hospitals as well. Due to what is labelled as an antiprofessional bias and an increased pressure for efficiency, psychiatrists have become 'glorified prescription writers' who are 'relegated to the role of technicians'.[13] Other mental health professionals are also seen to be affected by government funding cutbacks to state institutions as working conditions worsen, facilities deteriorate and roles become more narrowly defined.[14] For example, clinical psychologists are described as deprofessionalizing largely as a result of their employee status in bureaucracies where efficiency is key.[15,16,17]

Cohen and Wagner,[18] while not specifically employing the term deprofessionalization, describe the problems of social work professionalism, arguing that social work jobs are similar to jobs of other skilled workers because their salaries are low, their bargaining power is poor, their high caseloads necessitate assembly line work, they have limited autonomy in their work situation because the agency exercises considerable control, they have limited input into policy decisions, and there is a lack of opportunity for advancement. These problems are seen to arise principally because of bureaucratic organizations in government subject to cost rationalization, the growth of para-professional workers, and because these professionals primarily serve the poor and the working class.

Changes in other occupational groups have been described in a similar vein. For example, Tuckman, Caldwell and Vogler[19] and Van Arsdale[20] have discussed the deprofessionalization of university teaching, suggesting the presenting symptom of this problem is that there is an increasing number of part-time appointments to university faculty positions. The consequence of this use of part-timers is to restrict academic freedom (including freedom to choose texts and to develop one's own course materials and course schedules), to discourage teaching of a specialty, to deny participation in university governance, and to deny academics access to research funds.[21]

These examples of explanations of change are more aptly identified as deskilling, a concept which describes a broader, historical process of change affecting the organization of work. The deskilling thesis, developed by Braverman,[22] argued that the labour process was shaped by the accumulation of capital and that a dominant goal in profit-making was to purchase labour power as cheaply as possible. Thus, 'scientific management', or Taylorism, has come to dominate the world of production, bringing a qualitatively different dimension to control in which the manager dictates to the worker the precise manner in which work is to be done. The labour process then becomes dissociated from the actual skills of the worker, and the conception of the task becomes divorced from the execution of the task. In this way, management can cheapen the cost of the worker by decreasing his or her training and enlarging that employee's output. Braverman suggests that the analysis of the job begins to break up the process of work; and the detailed breakdown and division of job components dismembers the worker because it destroys the craft under the control of the worker. According to Braverman, professionals are not immune to this phenomenon.

With a renewed attention to measures for cost restraint in health care in most industrialized nations, nurses are faced with the increased pressures of scientific management techniques, including measurements of patient acuity levels, nursing workload, and so on. These techniques are commendable when they serve their intended purpose of enhancing the quality of care by improving decision-making. However, when these techniques become used as ends in themselves, or are used to effect cheaper and less effective levels of care, they become instruments of the deskilling of nurses because the craft and creativity of nursing is destroyed. White[23] has aptly described yet another process of the deskilling of nurses in her account of the devaluation of the quality of nurse training in England.

Deprofessionalization as proletarianization

Proletarianization, as an explanation of the changing professional role, is related to the deskilling thesis. Proletarianization of the worker is seen as a process through which an occupational group becomes divested of control over its work. Because work has lost its individual character and because specialized skills may be 'rendered valueless' by the invention of new approaches to production, workers can be easily replaced.

As applied to professionals, Derber[24] identifies three main structural features of proletarianization. First, advances in technology lead to the introduction of costly and complex machinery, and as technology becomes increasingly centralized, corporations and government institutions gradually extend their control over the technology to determine the terms and conditions of employment of those who use it. A second structural feature involves the continued expansion of professional services which then require a more centralized and enhanced administration to cope with the large numbers of clients. The invasion of professional markets by both public and private capital is the third structural feature which underlies the two previous states. The net result of this invasion is to make professionals subordinate to corporations and to make professionals employees of bureaucracies, increasingly a part of the subordination which other workers have long experienced.[25]

Derber[26,27] identifies two types of proletarianization: technical and ideological. He defines technical proletarianization as the workers' loss of control over the work itself, the means of labour. Technical proletarianization in this sense corresponds to Braverman's concept of deskilling since the worker's knowledge becomes expropriated as the task conception and task execution are separated. Ideological proletarianization, on the other hand, involves the worker's loss of control over the ends of his work, the goals and social purposes to which that work is directed. Thus, this type of proletarianization 'creates a type of worker whose integrity is threatened by the expropriation of his values and sense of purpose rather than his skill'.[28] This ideological proletarianization renders professionals 'powerless to choose or define the final product of one's work, its disposition in the market and its uses in the larger society, and the values or social policy of the organization which purchases one's labor'.[29]

Derber suggests that differentiating these types of proletarianization can provide a basis for understanding the position of professionals, particularly salaried professionals. He sees professionals as essentially subject to ideological proletarianization while increasingly vulnerable to technical proletarianization.[30] A prime example of ideological proletarianization might be the dilemma of the social worker as described by Specht.[31] He suggests that if social workers continue to adopt an activist stance and an advocacy role for their clients, their functions will be performed by other workers without social work qualifications since social work tasks are prescribed to serve organizational goals, essentially maintaining the status quo.

The proletarianization of professionals has commonly been discussed in the context of unionization and the use of union tactics by professionals. Perhaps a better understanding of the proletarianization theses can sensitize us to the frustrations many nurses experience when they feel they have lost control over the social purpose of their work (ideological proletarianization) and when they are denied the satisfaction of conceptualizing their nursing tasks but are instead directed to execute their tasks as prescribed by management (technical proletarianization).

Deprofessionalization as erosion of professional knowledge and trust

A third type of deprofessionalization discussed in the literature describes the change in the professions as based on an erosion of professional knowledge and skills, and a loss of public trust. Haug[32,33] defined deprofessionalization as 'a loss to professional occupations of their unique abilities, particularly their monopoly over knowledge, public belief in their service ethos, and expectations of work autonomy and authority over the client'.[34] Haug, supported by Toren,[35] based a thesis of deprofessionalization on a number of observations in which there appeared to be a challenge to the professional–client relationship,[36] and on extensive research on power relationships between physicians and patients.[37,38]

Priests and parish ministers have been discussed in this context of deprofessionalization. The move of priests and ministers from a narrow competency to multifaceted competencies (of preacher, teacher, administrator, organizer, church politician, etc.); the growth of alternate professionals (including social workers, teachers and lay ministers); the narrowed education gap between pastor and parishioner; the increasingly rational techniques within the church which de-mystify the role of the priest or minister; and an underlying secularization, have contributed to this deprofessionalization. The net effect of these trends is that priests and ministers no longer have a strong theoretical base, have lost a monopoly on exclusive skills and competencies, are increasingly guided by rules, and must satisfy the needs of the laity (as they define them) in order to maintain a congregation.[39,40]

Two problems indicative of the deprofessionalization of law in America are described by Rothman[41] as a weakened autonomy because of the legal misdeeds of Watergate, and challenges to the monopoly of expertise of lawyers by the range and variety of legal services now rendered by para-professionals. The causes of deprofessionalization rest in the narrowing of the competence gap between lawyers and their clients; the routinization of expert knowledge (by electronic data processing, do-it-yourself legal manuals, etc.); the increased specialization of lawyers; the changing demographics of the legal profession (i.e. away from the domination of white males); and the employment of lawyers in bureaucracies.

In an extensive analysis of deprofessionalization in nursing, Stinson[42] compared the social context of the times and the configuration of characteristics in nursing c. 1920 and c. 1960. She concluded that in the 1920s nursing was undergoing a process of professionalization for a number of reasons, including the relative integrity of the knowledge-skill component, 'substantial articulation of nursing roles with those of related personnel', and a relatively high degree of functional autonomy.[43] However, within the context of the 1960s, she concluded that the 'configuration of characteristics in nursing' appeared to be one type of deprofessionalization which she described as occupational disintegration. Reasons cited for this conclusion were based on a perceived

> deterioration of the substantive knowledge-skill component, a decline in the aura of mystery, lack of theoretical development and inadequate development of methodology suitable to research in nursing, and adaptations to technological innovations

which had served to take the nurse away from the patient, 'her chief locus of nursing knowledge'.[44] Stinson also observed that the nurses' increased responsibilities had not been accompanied by increases in authority, and that the socialization of recruits appeared to be poorly articulated with the complex organizational settings in which nurses worked. Stinson viewed this type of deprofessionalization ('diseased professionalism') as a dysfunctional, disintegrative force in society because the social need for nursing service and the state of the nursing profession were no longer in a good functioning relationship to each other.

Can deprofessionalization represent a desirable future?

Stinson described a second type of deprofessionalization as 'functional deprofessionalization'. This occurs when professions seek to reverse the situation in which a preoccupation with professional status has come to override a concern with their professional mission of putting knowledge to socially responsible uses. In this sense, the profession moves away from 'excessive professionalization' toward the normative state, a state consistent with a service ideal.

This concept of deprofessionalization is not unlike Anderson's[45] ideal in his plea that pharmacists return to a greater sense of mission by increasing their contact with patients, and Zimmerman's[46] call for the deprofessionalization of occupational therapists to counteract the negative effects of professionalization which he described as professional insularity, professional narcissism, trained incapacity, the overpricing of labour, and the dehumanization of students and other health practitioners. He suggested that de-mystifying professional roles would allow for a more effective health team strategy. Likewise, Illich[47] called for the deprofessionalization of medicine in order to unmask the myth according to which technical progress demands the solution of human problems by the application of scientific principles, the myth of benefit through an increase in the specialization of labor, through multiplication of arcane manipulations, and the myth that increasing dependence of people on the right of access to impersonal institutions is better than trust in one another.[48]

From a theoretical perspective, this functional deprofessionalization is a move against the trend predicted by Max Weber[49] that the over-emphasis on purposive-rational action would strip the world of its ethical meaning.[50] Weber had observed that the rationalization of life, which made advanced economic systems possible, served to contravene distinctive values of individuality, creativity and autonomy of Western society.[51,52] Taking Weber's concept of rationality as his starting point, Habermas[53] proposed the need to attend to different types of rationality including both the technical and the practical. Technical rationality, because it is oriented toward manipulating the objective world, allows man to acquire increasingly greater control over nature. Practical rationality is oriented towards interactions within the social world, governed by consensual norms. Out of a practical rationality there develops a greater ability to exercise personal power and to achieve a state of affairs where non-alienating work and free interactions are possible.[54] Habermas suggested that if human history was to evolve, it was essential that actions be oriented in specific directions which involved reference to both technical and practical rationalization.

As applied to the theses of deprofessionalization, proletarianization and deskilling, Habermas's thesis offers some direction. First, it suggests a need to move away from the deskilling and ideological proletarianization of all workers, including professionals, by a better balancing of technical rationality with practical rationality, a rationality involving attention to individual autonomy and creativity, and to meaningful human interaction.

Second, the thesis would suggest that such deprofessionalization is likely to be functional and may represent a desirable future. If professionalism has been dominated by purposive-rational action to the detriment of meaningful interaction, any move in the direction of greater practical rationality could only be positive. In relation to health professionals in particular, a common concern expressed by health-care consumers is that health care has become dehumanized because health professionals provide limited information to the patient, exhibit little apparent interest in the patient, allow for limited patient autonomy, and are all too frequently preoccupied with medical technology as opposed to a meaningful practitioner–patient exchange. As Betz and O'Connell[55] have stated, too often the doctor–patient relationship which should result in integration, consensus and trust leads instead to dissension, conflict and distrust:

> With the rationalization of technique and accompanying professionalization, doctors also became more oriented toward technical treatment of illness, ignoring the supportive, confidence-building and trusting dimension of the helping relationship. A split between technical rationality and interpersonal rationality developed.[56]

Betz and O'Connell argued for a rationalization of the exchange relations between producers (professionals) and consumers in which there would be greater clarity of goals, and the means of reaching the goals, and more client contribution to the exchange.

Nursing has taken a number of steps in the direction of a professionalism functional to society. In the development and testing of nursing theory nurses have worked to establish a foundation for safe and effective practice,[57] thus moving away from the type of deprofessionalization described by Stinson as occupational disintegration. And in identifying advocacy as a philosophical base for nursing[58] nurses have taken steps towards re-establishing their professional mission and have moved away from forms of excessive professionalization towards a functional deprofessionalization. A continued re-examination of the professional role to ensure it is socially relevant and responsive, and renewed attention to the humanistic dimension of nursing care will be necessary to effect a desirable future for nursing.

Conclusions

Deprofessionalization is a concept with many theoretical interpretations, all of which can provide nurses with a means of understanding changes occurring in the nursing profession. These various forms of deprofessionalization are likely to be manifested differently across time periods and across nations.

A greater sensitivity to the forms deprofessionalization may take can alert nursing administrators, nursing educators and nursing practitioners to problems which impede effective nursing practice. For example, nurse administrators must guard against practices which foster the deskilling of nurses, and they must seek to represent nurses more effectively at the upper levels of managerial decision-making, particularly when those decisions impact on nursing. In addition, finding ways for greater participation of nursing staff in such decision-making is critical to ensuring that nurses feel a sense of control over the goals and social purposes of their work. Likewise, nurse educators will need to continue to advocate standards of nursing education which can enhance the contribution and the creativity of nursing practitioners.

Stinson's identification of functional and dysfunctional deprofessionalization serves further to clarify developments in the professionalization of nursing. In that the concept of functional deprofessionalization embodies the idea of a normative state, it represents a desirable form of deprofessionalization because it is a move to re-establish the social mission of nursing.

References

1. Wilensky, H. L., 'The professionalization of everyone?', *American Journal of Sociology*, 1964, **70**, No. 2, 137–158.
2. Goode, W. J., 'The theoretical limits of professionalization'. In A. Etizioni (ed.), *The Semi-Professions and Their Organization*. The Free Press, New York, 1969, pp. 216–313.
3. Barber, B., 'Some problems in the sociology of the professions', *Daedalus*, 1963, **92**, 669–688.
4. Bell, D., *The Coming of Post-Industrial Society*. Basic Books, New York, 1973.
5. See reference 2, p. 277.
6. Johnson, T. J., *Professions and Power*. Macmillan, London, 1972.
7. Larson, M. S., *The Rise of Professionalism*. University of California Press, Berkeley, 1977.
8. Haug, M. R., 'The deprofessionalization of everyone?' *Sociological Focus*, 1975, **8**, 197–213.
9. Derber, C., *Professionals as Workers: Mental Labor in Advanced Capitalism*. G. K. Hall, Boston, 1982.
10. Fink, P. J. and Weinstein, S. P., 'Whatever happened to psychiatry? The deprofessionalization of community mental health services', *American Journal of Psychiatry*, 1979, **136**, 406–409.
11. Miller, R. T., Mazade, N. A., Muller, S. and Andrulis, D., 'Trends in community mental health programming', *American Journal of Community Psychology*, 1978, **6** (April), 191–198.
12. See reference 10, p. 407.
13. 'Commentary—De-hospitalization and de-professionalism', *Psychiatric Annals*, 1978, **8**, No. 12, 58–64.
14. Silverman, W. H., 'The evolving mental health professions: Psychiatric social work, clinical psychology, psychiatry and psychiatric nursing', *Journal of Mental Health Administration*, 1985, **12**, No. 2, 28–31.

15. Dabbs, A. R., 'The apparent propensity towards the de-professionalization of clinical psychology', *Bulletin of the British Psychological Society*, 1982, **35**, 460–461.
16. Kat, B., 'The deprofessionalization of clinical psychology: A reply to Dabbs', *Bulletin of the British Psychological Society*, 1983, **36** (May), 162–163.
17. McPherson, D., 'The deprofessionalization of clinical psychology', *Bulletin of the British Psychological Society*, 1983, **36** (Feb), 63–64.
18. Cohen, M. B. and Wagner, D., 'Social work professionalism: Reality and illusion'. In Derber, 1982, see reference 9.
19. Tuckman, H. P., Caldwell, J. and Vogler, W., 'Part-timers and the academic labor market of the eighties', *American Sociologist*, 1978, **13**, No. 4, 184–195.
20. Van Arsdale, G., 'Deprofessionalizing a part-time teaching faculty: How many, feeling small, seeming few, getting less, dream of more', *American Sociologist*, 1978, **13**, No. 4, 195–201.
21. See reference 20.
22. Braverman, H., *Labor and Monopoly Capital: The Degradation of Work in the Twentieth Century*. Monthly Review, New York, 1974.
23. White, R., 'Educational entry requirements for nurse registration: an historical perspective', *Journal of Advanced Nursing*, 1985, **10**, 583–590.
24. See reference 9.
25. See reference 9.
26. See reference 9.
27. Derber, C., 'Managing professionals: Ideological proletarianization and post-industrial labor', *Theory and Society*, 1983, **12**, 309–341.
28. See reference 9, p. 172.
29. See reference 27, p. 313.
30. See reference 9.
31. Specht, H., 'The deprofessionalization of social work', *Social Work*, 1972, **17**, No. 2, 3–15.
32. Haug, M. R., 'De-professionalization: An alternate hypothesis for the future', *Sociological Review Monograph*, 1973, **20**, 195–211.
33. See reference 8.
34. See reference 32, p. 197.
35. Toren, N., 'De-professionalization and its sources', *Sociology of Work and Occupations*, 1975, **2**, 323–337.
36. Haug, M. R. and Sussman, M. B., 'Professional autonomy and the revolt of the client', *Social Problems*, 1969, **17**, 153–161.
37. Haug, M. R., 'The erosion of professional authority: a cross-cultural inquiry in the case of the physician', *Milbank Memorial Fund Quarterly*, 1976, **6**, 83–106.
38. Haug, M. R. and Lavin, B., *Consumerism in Medicine: Challenging Physician Authority*. Sage Publications, Beverly Hills, 1983.
39. Jarvis, P., 'The parish ministry as a semi-profession', *Sociological Review*, 1975, **23**, No. 4, 911–922.
40. Goldner, F. H., Ference, T. P. and Ritti, R. R., 'Priests and laity: a profession in transition'. In P. Halmos (ed.), *Professionalization and Social*

Change. The Sociological Review Monograph, J. H. Brookes, Staffs, pp. 119–137.

41. Rothman, R. A., 'Deprofessionalization: The case of law in America', *Work and Occupations*, 1984, **11** (May), 183–206.
42. Stinson, S. M., *Deprofessionalization in Nursing*. Ed.D. dissertation. Columbia University, New York, 1969.
43. See reference 42, p. 378.
44. See reference 42, p. 378.
45. Anderson, R. D., 'The peril of deprofessionalization', *American Journal of Hospital Pharmacists*, 1977, **34**, 133–139.
46. Zimmerman, T. F., 'Is professionalization the answer to improving health care?' *American Journal of Occupational Therapy*, 1974, **28**, 465–468.
47. Illich, I., *Medical Nemesis—The Expropriation of Health*. Pantheon Books, New York, 1976.
48. See reference 47, p. 256.
49. Gerth, H. and Mills, C. W., *From Max Weber: Essays in Sociology*. Oxford University Press, New York, 1946.
50. Habermas, J., *The Theory of Communicative Action: Volume 1. Reason and the Rationalization of Society*. Beacon Press, Boston, 1984.
51. Weber, M., *The Protestant Ethic and the Spirit of Capitalism*. Charles Scribner and Sons, New York, 1958.
52. Giddens, A., *Capitalism and Modern Social Theory: An Analysis of the Writings of Marx, Durkheim and Max Weber*. Cambridge University Press, Cambridge, 1971.
53. Habermas, J., *Towards a Rational Society*. Beacon Press, Boston, 1970.
54. Bernstein, R. J., *The Restructuring of Social and Political Theory*. Harcourt Brace Jovanovich, New York, 1976.
55. Betz, M. and O'Connell, L., 'Changing doctor–patient relationships and the rise in concern for accountability', *Social Problems*, 1983, **31**, No. 1, 84–95.
56. See reference 55, p. 89.
57. Gruending, D. L., 'Nursing theory: a vehicle of professionalization', *Journal of Advanced Nursing*, 1985, **10**, 553–558.
58. Curtin, L., 'The nurse as advocate: a philosophical foundation for nursing', *Advances in Nursing Science*, 1979, **1**, No. 3, 1–10.

Political Issues in Nursing: Past, Present and Future, Volume 3
Edited by R. White
© 1988 John Wiley & Sons Ltd

CHAPTER 4

Accounting for care: a framework for analysing change in Canadian Nursing

MARIE L. CAMPBELL, RN, PhD
*Research Fellow, Faculty of Social Sciences, Carleton University, Ottawa,
Canada, K1S 5B6*

Knowledge and control

This chapter is about the exercise of control, as an objective practice in which nurses participate, in hospitals and other workplaces, and in professional associations. It draws on theoretical and empirical work in the 'social organization of knowledge', including the author's research in the social organization of nursing information systems.[1] My aim is to map changes in Canadian nursing within a framework in which socially-constructed information about nursing, used in documentary methods of decision-making, can be seen as a central feature. The view of nursing which I present suggests an alternative research programme.

Nursing operates in an organizational milieu highly structured by documents. Making observations of patients and recording them has always been part of nurses' work, but the last few decades have brought an increasing reliance on the use of documents. This is a general feature of organizational action in contemporary Western industrialized societies which sociologist Dorothy Smith speaks of as 'textually-

I gratefully acknowledge the receipt of a fellowship from the Social Sciences and Humanities Research Council of Canada, which supported part of the research for this chapter; Alice Baumgart, Nancy Jackson, Lynn Kirkwood and George Smith made helpful comments on an earlier draft.

mediated social organization'.[2] Definite documentary procedures have been developed, Smith says, to transpose personal acts into organizational ones.

> Progressively over the last hundred years a system of organizational consciousness has been produced expressing knowledge in a documentary mode and transposing what were formerly individual judgments, hunches, guesses and so on into formulae for analysing data or making assessments. Such practices render organizational judgment, feedback, information and coordination into objectified documentary rather·than subjective processes.[3]

In nursing, the development of such 'formulae' as Nursing Care Plans, Patient Classification Systems and Nursing Audits has been relatively recent. The capacity to make individual judgements transpersonal, objective and co-ordinated, through documents, is the route to new forms of organized action. Documentary processes are used to

> execute, control, regulate, inform and order, in the various sites of governing, management, administration, discursive relations, professional associations, etc., form[ing] a loosely coordinated apparatus that we will call the ruling apparatus.[4]

This chapter is written for nurses who have felt uneasy with the mismatch between what is officially known and said about nursing, and how it is known in the lived experience of nurses who are confused and angry about what is being done to them in the name of improving 'quality of nursing care', 'efficiency' and 'the status of nursing'. I want to draw an analogy between the power of documentary knowledge of nursing and Dale Spender's description of the oppressive force of 'man made language'[5] in women's lives. In nursing, the knowledge/language/control nexus is not gender organized, although gender differences in nursing and health care have other well-known oppressive outcomes.[6] However, the privilege of knowing and speaking authoritatively is the means by which a division is being organized in Canadian nursing. Smith's[7] analysis of the conceptual imperialism involved in male dominance in academia is instructive here. Nurses are moving from their traditional subordinate place in health care, into its ruling apparatus, previously a male domain. They are developing a knowledge base which provides for their entry and participation. Speaking about sociology, and the academic professions, Smith points out that a discipline's knowledge base is assembled with a set of procedures which detach it from practitioners:

> The ethic of objectivity and the methods used in its practice are concerned primarily with the separation of the knower from what he knows and in particular with the separation of what is known from any interests, 'biases', etc., which are not the interests and concerns authorized by the discipline. . . . Entering the governing mode . . . lifts the actor out of the immediate local and particular place in which he is in the body. He uses what becomes present to him in this place as a means to pass beyond it to the conceptual order. This mode of action creates . . . a bifurcated consciousness. . . . It establishes two modes of knowing and experiencing and doing, one located in the body and in the space which it occupies and moves into, the other which passes beyond it.[8]

Smith uses the pronoun 'he' consciously, because she is reporting on the work of male sociologists (to which female sociologists may contribute); both traditionally, and as a matter of occupational practices in our society, men appropriate the governing conceptual mode and assign women to the world organized by what Smith calls the natural attitude. Women's work liberates men from having to attend to bodily realities, so that they do not interfere with men's occupation of the conceptual sphere and the ideas they produce from that special site. Women's perspective, grounded in material conditions, provides a critique, which reveals that knowledge produced in this 'objective' way is partial, and not independent of the knower. 'Its conceptual procedures, methods and relevances are seen to organize its subject matter from a determinate position in society'[9]—a male ruling position.

This chapter explores the social organization of authorized knowledge about nursing, and its uses for management, planning, policy formulation and implementation. The second section describes, from my own research findings, two nursing management systems through which concepts used for 'ruling' nursing are detached from their ground in the actual or 'natural' work setting and are constructed to fit managerial decision-making processes. These systems are typical of the organizational practices which constitute the administrative reform nursing is currently undergoing. The third and fourth sections take up the reform theme, looking first at its earlier manifestations and then at some of its contemporary features. These sections offer glimpses of how·objective decision-making processes are penetrating the relations between nurses.

What emerges is a series of questions, not yet satisfactorily answered, about the direction nursing is taking. The final section suggests the usefulness of a research programme in which policy and politics are topics for empirical inquiry.

It has seemed both timely and necessary for nursing to develop a discourse base for its education and practice. Both have moved from being organized around an accumulation of experience to being conceptually-based. Twenty years ago in Canada, nursing was taught as a set of procedures associated with medical diagnoses; now, discourse-based nursing is taught through curricula organized around a conceptual model of nursing. Now, too, nursing practice relies on nurses developing conceptual skills for assessing their patients' needs and taking appropriate action according to a systematic ordering of nursing priorities. The evolution of such conceptual frameworks for nursing has been an undertaking of nursing academics whose own interests as intellectuals within the university community have revolved around making nursing into a discourse-based discipline. Ideas about nursing are now authorized through the same discursive means as other academic subjects, that is, through reference to a professional research-grounded literature. The official nursing bodies in Canada have played a part in getting this approach accepted and implemented in nursing.[10] University nurses have generally promoted it.

The shift to a discourse base for nursing was intended both to modernize and to improve professional practice. Health-oriented models of nursing, for instance, broaden nurses' views of what nursing should. be offering patients. But new control capacities incorporated into nursing practice have also been influential in changing nursing. Nursing's conceptual base makes it possible for nurses to be trained to make decisions objectively and to be held accountable for them. Documentary methods of objective decision-making, including methods of demonstrating accountability, have seemed to offer an answer to the problems of increasing unmanageability of large institutions, the speeded-up movement of patients through them, as well as the increasing volume of specialized knowledge with which nurses, to be effective, need to have some familiarity. Improvements in nursing were hoped for through effecting better control, related to a general tightening up of hospital management. The new nursing management systems allow implementation of centrally-developed policy, especially fiscal policy. In making the necessary internal adjustment to fiscal restraint, the new documentary methods of control over nursing have been an important adjunct.

Documentary management of hospital nursing

The 1984 doctoral study by the author[11] analysed two document-based nursing management systems operating in a community hospital in Ontario. One, an objective workload measurement and staffing system, provides decision-making capacity for nurse staffing in relation to patients' needs for care. The other deals with clinical nursing practice and objective evaluation of its outcome, and is called a 'quality assurance' system. Each of the decision-making processes is composed of a set of nursing records within an information-processing system. In each system, described below, an accounting use is made of information generated in specially formated nursing records. The accounting procedures for making decisions 'objectively' require that two phemonena be brought into commensurable relation with each other. In the study cited, textual analysis explicated how the documents accomplish the relation between the two phenomena *as a conceptual matter*.[12] In each case, the phenomena to be related in the decision-making process were seen to be more malleable in their conceptual than in their material form, a feature of the systems which has special significance, as will be discussed below.

Workload measurement and staffing system

Patient Classification[13] is the name of a management device which controls the definition of 'need' for nursing care, the concept central to organizing the objective and efficient management of nursing labour. A Patient Classification system offers a hospital increased control over the productive capacity of its nursing labour force. Efficiency in applying professional labour to a body of nursing work depends upon management's capacity to control the nurse-hours expended per patient. Patient Classification 'works' as a control mechanism through making objective a heretofore individual professional judgement about patients' needs for nursing care. A documentary process (a classification of patients by need levels) systematically transforms nurses' professional knowledge into cost-relevant terms. Objective needs, as generated in the documentary system, can be addressed by management according to cost criteria, thus displacing reliance on individual nurses' professional criteria which are neither standardized nor cost-driven. A number of management priorities for planning and control can be accommodated on the basis of the objective data. Importantly, standardized estimates of the work to be done can be used to spread a sparse nursing labour force equitably across hospital units and to move staff in response to fluctuations in need. Also, nurse staffing can be adjusted to meet needs *as budget allows*, rather then as nurses' professional judgement dictates.

The construction of an objective statement of needs to replace nurses' professional judgement requires that nurses participate, on a daily basis, in the documentary process of estimating and standardizing their patients' needs for care. In a set of records comprising an 'information system', nurses record plans for their patient's therapeutic regime, nursing actions, observations, and so on. The Patient Classification Form takes as *indicators* specific aspects of what nurses know about their patients, to refer back to research findings of Time and Activity Studies (in the research work, standard times for doing standard tasks have been established in research settings). Patients with similar features, noted in Patient Classification indicators, are grouped in one of several levels of care. Levels or classifications denote average allotments of time for an averaged selection of nursing tasks for patients with those features.

Standardization is the essential feature in the objective determination of 'levels of care' in patient classification. Classifying patients into levels of need for care helps create a sufficiently stable data basis for prediction and comparison of workloads, in a work setting characterized by a high degree of control by front-line workers over knowledge of the work process. (They have been able to control it precisely because of its rapidly shifting and unstable character.) Objective data are created by paring off the differences among patients within classification levels, as well as making it possible, indeed necessary, systematically to ignore differences among individual nurses.

The process of standardization also gives management some input into how much nursing care is enough. This can be done when specific data about individual patients are *generalized* in the Patient Classification documents, then transferred to management for rationalizing the allocation of paid labour time in relation to budget 'realities'. The capacity of the workload measurement and staffing system to make patients' needs for care fit constrained budgets comes from the system's documentary character. The documents stabilize or 'objectify' need for care, something which in real or experiential terms is not stable. Any disjuncture between documentary accounts and the real world as nurses and patients experience it can be 'solved' on paper. Of course, any such disjunctures remain as problems to be accommodated in the workplace interactions of nurses and patients. In the documentation, the concept 'needs' loses its material connection to real patients and gains its character of being adjustable to management's cost-constrained 'realities'. What constitutes good enough care, previously a professional judgement, becomes established by how much staff (time) is made available. When the system provides less time than nurses think is enough, their judgement is challenged by the 'official version' generated in the staffing system. Indeed nurses' voices are silenced, because only the documentary knowledge is able to be entered into decision-making processes. This is one way in which efficiency measures can have troublesome effects.

The 'quality assurance' system

Quality Assurance is the name given to a system for objectively controlling nursing practice actions and outcomes through a set of record-keeping, monitoring and feedback processes.[14] The system aims at organizing 'effectiveness' into nurses' work through documentary means similar to those used to organize 'efficiency' as discussed above. In specifically formated documents, nurses record each step of their work, making it accessible to evaluation. The categories of the recording forms reflect professional Standards of Practice, more or less explicitly. When nurses transpose their plans and actions into the records, they make their work objectively 'accountable'. The record can be compared to a written standard, offering a method for establishing an accountably adequate level of quality (when the forms are filled out properly). Nurses' accountability for practice decisions, and for the outcomes of specific nursing acts, gains a documentary basis, which because it means altering the whole labour process of nursing to make it conceptual, has been quite a challenge for nurses to adjust to. For a number of years, 'Nursing Process',[15] 'Nursing Diagnosis'[16] and 'Nursing Care Plans'[17] have been on the nursing agenda for in-service training; nursing curricula have been reorganized to gather up what is taught under a proper conceptual 'model of nursing';[18] academics in nursing faculties have developed and debated the merits of various 'nursing theories'.[19] The profession has committed itself to developing a knowledge base in which nursing can be made accountable.

Accountability, in this article, is being explicated as *a management practice* in which records are monitored and words are matched. Because 'results' are produced in documentary form, record-keeping has taken on a new importance in nursing. Document-based Quality Assurance systems could not have been implemented had not the profession, particularly its academic arm, busied itself with the theoretical and conceptual work of recent years. Systematic ordering of ideas about nursing (in 'nursing theory') provides the conceptual basis for all the administrative control procedures organized as 'accountability'.

Important decisions now rest on the use of accountability information. I found two kinds of problems with the systems. One, discussed above, has to do with the control associated with objective decision-making, especially over staffing, and where that control resides. 'Quality' may have to be generated in conditions which are not conducive to good care. Also, and this is the second kind of problem, documents may not accurately reflect the nature of the work being done. 'Quality' (like 'needs' in the staffing system), when generated through a documentary course of action, has an ideal form which may be different from what nurses know about their work from where they stand. The capacity inherent in the documentary 'supervisory' system is expected to bring nurses' activities into line with standards, through their adherence to an approved recording format. It is true that nurses are required to produce records in which 'quality' can be found, as a first priority of their jobs under objective management. The idea behind the 'supervisory' use of documents is that *actions taken* will reflect nurses' recording practices. However, under pressure to improve their documentation, nurses may adjust their record-keeping, but not their practice. Especially as time constraints interfere with what they can actually get done in a workday, nurses may simply produce records which pass inspection. Audit of such records would produce unwarranted confidence in the quality of care given.

Hospital managements are in the position of needing documentary guarantees of the quality of professional practice.[20] As the incidence of coroner's inquests rises (and as conditions in hospitals become potentially dangerous under restrained budgets), Quality Assurance systems have their own justification. They offer objective assurance that proper management is in place and they defer blame from the organization and its managers when untoward incidents happen. Unfortunately, documentary accountability systems do not always work to deter blame from front-line nurses; the detailed recording nurses are required to do identifies the individual nurse and her actions and/or expected actions. She remains responsible for *actual* outcomes of care, in whatever conditions she has been given to work. Conflated in the systems are the managerial control and the professional control prerogatives, with the latter being subordinated to the former.[21] If a mistake has been made, or the nurse has had to skip certain tasks as she stretches herself over more patients (to improve productivity), she becomes personally liable for the trouble that causes. In such cases, the management systems, reflecting the documentary version of need for care, may show staffing to be 'adequate' and may even offer a reading of 'quality' care being given.

The profession is turning to accountability systems for solution of their own control requirements (mandated through legislation in Canadian provinces). For example, the College of Nurses of Ontario has the responsibility of enforcing a regulation which requires nurses to 'exercise generally accepted standards of practice . . .' and to 'maintain nursing records for the persons for whom [the nurse] performs the nursing service';[22] this requirement articulates with the clause of the legislation which gives the College the right to make regulations governing standards of practice for the profession;[23] built into this wording of the Act is an understanding that the profession's responsibilities for 'regulating' the practice of nursing can and will be carried out through documentary practices. The College fulfils its responsibilities by producing written standards,[24] which can be used as guides in the development of hospital management systems. It provides the conceptualizations of 'quality' care, but not the testing of actual care. The College 'subcontracts' to hospital employers and their management systems, the profession's responsibility for maintaining adequacy of nursing standards of practice. As part of the 'subcontractual' arrangement, the profession implicitly endorses the intensification of nurses' work which the cost-driven nature of the management systems organizes. The 'blind spot' that the profession maintains about this organized outcome of management control over nursing may be partially accounted for by examining (as I do next) the emerging problem of divided interests in the profession regarding management priorities.

In professional circles, the notion that there might be a division of interests among nurses is more or less ignored.[25] Yet nursing's divided interests are becoming more pronounced as the nature of control in health-care organizations changes. The change being described is from traditional professional control, which is individually exercised, to managerial control which is lodged in documentary systems and is exercised in objective processes. I have argued elsewhere[26] that specific control technology directly affects the social relations of nursing. The introduction of accounting processes into non-profit (service-oriented) organizations creates a situation analogous in important ways to that found in capitalist production workplaces. My contention is that *the relations* between those controlled by the new methods and those implementing and operating them are also restructured. Differences in outlook, priorities, and so on arising between nurses who are part of the same profession and the same professional organizations are structured by their work. Satisfactory performance appraisals and promotions hinge on learning and playing the appropriate role, for instance. Nurses' own careers depend upon adopting management priorities.

Nursing's regulatory bodies (these may be provincial professional associations or, in Ontario, the College of Nurses) fail to recognize such differences in interests. Much of their influence over nurses is 'moral', based on codes of conduct and prescriptive documents, and at an even farther remove, in exercising their obligation to approve nursing curricula. Other than their statutory obligation and power to certify practitioners and to hear complaints and exercise discipline, the regulatory bodies have little actual control over nurses' daily practice. Nurses are socialized through professional training to cleave, in their individual decisions and actions, to the profession's beliefs and practices. Maintenance of a unitary view of the profession is a necessary part of keeping (subordinate) nurse employees acting in line with professional ideals which may not be in their own interests. For instance, a strong professional ideology makes nurses intensify their efforts to care for all their assigned patients, when their staffing allocation is too low (i.e. when it has been lowered to reflect 'efficiency' concerns of the hospital). Nurses' professional commitment is actually relied on and cynically used against them in hospitals' efforts to contain costs. A less ideologically prepared workforce would stop work when their paid worktime was finished, whereas nurses routinely work overtime, routinely speed up their work, skip coffee breaks, and so on *to take good care of their patients.*[27]

Organizationally, nurses are not united. Their competence to practise is certified through official bodies in each province; in most, certification also carries with it membership in a professional association. In addition, most non-management nurses are members of unions, certified through labour laws to bargain collectively for their members. A wave of unionization in the 1970s increased the number of unionized nurses reported to be employed in 1984 to 127 284,[28] out of a total of 187 918.[29] Collective bargaining has increased the 1985 Canadian annual salary (in the United Nurses of Alberta collective agreement), to $27 611.00, then the highest pay for an entry-level Registered Nurse position.[30] The success of nursing unions in increasing nurses' earnings made implementation of hospital management 'efficiency measures' more crucial. In the mid-1970s, as hospital budgets began to be restrained, with particular attention on the nursing labour budgets, nurses' unions began to take positions on 'safety to practise' issues. In a landmark case, the Ontario nurses' union, the Ontario Nurses' Association, won a decision against a Toronto hospital where nurses had claimed understaffing made their practice unsafe.[31] A clause was inserted into the collective agreement providing a formal process through which nurses could be heard on issues of 'professional responsibility'. This was recognition that nurses' professional interests were not being adequately represented or advocated through existing routes. Since that time nurses' unions across the country have adopted similar methods.[32] These union-sponsored struggles against hospital managements whose fiscal difficulties are being addressed through attempting to squeeze more work out of nurses are a reminder that quality of nursing care is inextricably bound up with economic issues. Labour organizations have demonstrated that they have a legitimate interest in mediating professional practice problems.[33]

The professional associations carry the responsibility to advance 'the status of nursing' and in most provinces to regulate the practice of nursing. As regulators, they have played an instrumental role in reordering nursing for objective control and 'subcontracting' their regulatory function to managerial processes. Their strong belief in professional accountability through these documentary controls reflects a number of features in contemporary Canadian nursing; operating in the lee of medicine, nursing has grasped at the proffered accounting methods to legitimate and make objective the content and quality of nursing services. The systematization represented in accounting practices is viewed as a step up towards a scientific and more professionally credible practice.

In the next section, the influence of the university in bringing 'science' into nursing practice and policy is sketched. The weight of opinion about university education for nurses has shifted recently, with the official professional bodies now endorsing and actively supporting baccalaureate entry-to-practice. My analytic framework suggests that as the profession transforms itself and becomes organized in relation to documentary modes of action, fundamental differences will be noted between the profession's ruling ideas and the experience of practitioners who stay rooted in 'the natural attitude'. In the rest of the chapter, I highlight some of the progress towards a documentary mode of organizing nursing, indicating the nature of the divisions being created. The kind of research which would explicate the social organization of these differences has not yet been undertaken.

The university and the 'science' of nursing

The university has always played an important part in the struggle to bring Canadian nursing out of its subordination to medicine and give it a proper professional stance. Baumgart[34] notes that university nursing education was organized, originally, around reformist ideals of the early twentieth century related to scientific management, public health and pedagogy. In an otherwise sexist environment, predominantly hostile to higher education for nurses, university programmes undertook nursing's reform goals of

> giving nursing a respectable scientific and humanistic knowledge base; recruiting a higher calibre of students; improving the material and physical conditions of the work of the nurse; and penetrating and achieving improvements in the hundreds of hospital training schools which formed the bulk of nursing's preparatory educational system.[35]

Canadian university nursing programmes focused initially on these goals through developing nursing leaders, with expectations of a trickle-down effect. Now, however, it appears that the university is leading a reform of nursing which penetrates the profession in a different way. Effort has been extended beyond the original curriculum goal of improving the nurse's scientific (medical) knowledge; their conceptual skills are now equally important. The university plays the key role in formulating a conceptual base for nursing practice and is currently organizing curriculum design and instruction around new conceptual models of nursing.[36] Nursing theories are the product of academic work which attempts to specify the relationships between concepts and interventions, as an aid to nursing decision-making.

Recently, university education for nurses has taken a very high policy profile within the profession. A policy requiring baccalaureate entry-to-practice for all nurses educated in 2000 and beyond has become the focus of concerted promotion by the Canadian Nurses' Association (CNA). A National Plan for Entry to Practice, detailing strategic actions to be taken, was adopted by the CNA Board of Directors in February 1984.[37] Operating on a budget of $75 575, for its first year, it was staffed by a full-time co-ordinator, given two days' (per week) of support staff time.[38] Its objectives included promotion of the idea of baccalureate education for all nurses and assistance to (provincial) member associations in whose jurisdictions actual agreements had to be reached with employers and, most importantly, with educational and health-care funding authorities. Specific lobbying efforts were to be carried out with 'politicians, civil servants, health care professionals, and related groups'.[39] An *ad hoc* committee of educators was set up to develop 'marketing' strategies for the concept of baccalaureate entry-to-practice; consultants were hired to prepare cost analyses, and so on. A monthly newsletter was instituted to offer supportive information for 'argumentation' in support of baccalaureate entry-to-practice. The *Entry To Practice Newsletter* issued calls for research, and advice on research funding, for studies to demonstrate the benefits of baccalaureate nursing. In short, the CNA has committed itself wholeheartedly to baccalaureate entry-to-practice.

This policy could be a profession-initiated reform directed at improving nursing's occupational status; or it could be a response to environment pressures, or both. The argument that I am able to make about this is tentative and begins from the assumption that what the university is providing meets a perceived need, at least on the part of the organized profession. In this section, I look at what is happening in nursing that could be making university education for all nurses seem to be desirable and implementable.

Nursing has had to live with the dilemma created by articulation of its practice to a dominant male profession and the stigma associated with female work and femininity. The profession has wanted to move from a handmaiden role, with its low economic and intellectual status, to an independent practitioner role. To do that, it was felt that the nurse should be (educated to be seen as) knowledgeable, skilful and socially competent, enough to assert the (new) claims of her discipline in the professionally competitive world of twentieth-century health care.[40] Both the development of a knowledge base which could be seen as scientific and the acquisition of relevant social skills for asserting professional claims have been associated with university education. In addition, in working towards greater autonomy from the medical profession, nursing has taken responsibility for self-regulation. Both as a self-governing profession under provincial laws and as individual exployees or independent practitioners, nurses have been expected (and expect themselves) to demonstrate accountability for their practice. The new discourse-based methods of providing documentary links between actions and ideas have become the *modus operandi* of professional accountability.

Along with the technologies for demonstrating accountability, nurses have needed to define roles from which to practise more independently. Strengthening nurses' theoretical basis for independent decision-making was an integral part, along with additional skills training, of university preparation for the 'expanded role'.[41] That innovation failed to thrive in the medically dominated health-care system. Neither did it engender the support of the profession for baccalaureate preparation which we are seeing now.

The professional associations, particularly the Canadian Nurses' Association, have developed political strategies for inserting the image of the nurse as an autonomous professional into health policy frameworks. The CNA's lobbying and 'interest group' interventions in the health-policy field during the past few years have focused on a primary care role for nurses. The primary care role concept is built on the same educational groundwork as the expanded role. It has been put forward in a manner which attempts to organize government support *against* medical control over health care, in the interests of nurses.[42] This represents a new coalition between nurses as 'corporate rationalizers'[43] and others in the health-care field who are primarily concerned with fiscal issues. Success as independent practitioners depends on more than nurses' training to work in primary care. The new Canada Health Act extends the possibility of insurance coverage to more categories of health-care practitioners. If provincial plans (partially funded through federal transfer payments) include nursing as insured services, nurses may bill directly for their services. However, physicians' resistance to giving up to nurses even small pieces of a lucrative field of practice must be overcome, and there is no sign of that happening; also to make a primary care role viable for more than a few nurses, government monies must be invested in a community-based delivery system. This is not likely to happen while existing acute and extended (chronic) care services are seriously underfunded and stretched to the limit due to fiscal restraint policies.[44] Patients, precipitately discharged from hospitals, are being dumped into the care of female family members.[45] Privately organized and scantily trained and supervised home helpers are now doing work previously done by or under the supervision of professional nurses. Nurses seem to be losing ground in this field, not gaining. It is probably not justifiable to insist on baccalaureate education for all nurses on the grounds that it prepares them for primary care roles.

A stronger justification for changes in nurses' basic education lies in the belief, especially if it were to be empirically supported, that nursing care, given by nurses with university degrees, is better than care given by nurses with different kinds of preparation. This argument is likely to appeal to a wider spectrum of the profession than those interested solely in preparation of an independent practitioner. Hospital nursing administrators have always been pragmatic about their staffing needs, wanting to hire nurses who were ready to fulfil job requirements. They need nurses fully attuned to the new realities of hospital life. The growing importance to hospital administration of objective means of affirming that acceptable standards of care are met may be revising some of the traditional ideas about suitable preparation. Educational grounding in using conceptual models, which is promoted in modern educational programmes, develops the nurse's competence in the new objective mode of administration. Nurses must now be able and willing to reinterpret their experience to make it fit conceptual forms which are 'accountable'.

As reformers, nurse educators feel a certain amount of passion for the work they believe is going to help liberate their students from medical dominance. Attridge sees the results as 'curriculum iatrogenesis'.[46] Students in university programmes are inculcated with a strong belief in the objective mode, often over their objections, and even to the extent that it interferes with their acquisition of skills and credibility with other technically competent nurses.[47] Nurse educators, in enforcing the nursing discourse version of reality, are training their students to deny their experience in favour of objective ways of knowing.

University nursing programmes have been designed to prepare nurses for entry positions in nursing, not leadership positions, since the early 1970s. But that view has been accepted only recently by the provincial professional associations. As recently as the mid-1970s, the proper role of a baccalaureate-prepared nurse was the subject of a dispute between a provincial nursing association, the Registered Nurses' Association of Ontario (RNAO) and the Ontario regional association of the Canadian Association of University Schools of Nursing (ORCAUSN).[48] University-trained nurses know how to engage in discourse-based interaction, in the professionally sanctioned framework nursing science has constructed.[49] This doubtless fits them more smoothly into their roles in health-care institutions whose managements are part of the contemporary 'ruling apparatus'.

Seeing the integration of a management function within the professional practice of nursing suggests another way to think about the usefulness of university education for all nurses. Implicit in the plan to upgrade nursing education by making a university degree the entry-to-practice requirement is its 'classing' effect on the profession. Nurses have always been recruited from all socio-economic sectors. But recruitment into university programmes channels girls from different populations into nursing. University accessibility problems in Canada, recently documented by academic studies[50] and the Canadian Federation of Students,[51] reduce the chances for girls from low-income or ethnic families, or from rural and certain geographic regions, getting into university. Work-subsidized training in hospital schools has always been as available to girls from low-income families as to middle-class girls. The demise of these schools in the wealthiest provinces followed the economic boom of the 1950s and the building of a community college system which offered technical education, including (the diploma in) nursing, at affordable fees. Hospital (diploma) schools still operate in less affluent parts of the country, recruiting students who cannot afford university education. In 1981, less than 8 per cent of employed registered and graduate nurses working in New Brunswick, for instance, had been educated in university programmes.[52] In Ontario, the province with the strongest economy, the figure was 11 per cent for the same period.[53] By 1984, according to statistics collected by the Canadian Nurses Association, of the 187 918 nurses employed in nursing across Canada, 11 per cent (or 20 663 nurses) had university degrees in nursing.[54] Of those employed in hospitals, 90.9 per cent did not have degrees in 1984.[55] While the profession has not explicitly addressed the question 'is a recruit from a middle-class home necessarily a "better calibre" nurse?' it may be that this apparently outmoded, elitist idea still has some utility in the increasingly tense hospital labour milieu.

Implementation of tighter labour process controls in hospital nursing has created a manager–worker climate replacing the more co-operative nursing work unit. Labour unrest among nurses has followed. It is quite conceivable that university training is seen by administrators as more conducive to proper professional socialization than diploma school training. Nursing administrators, now themselves increasingly university-educated, are being rallied in support of university education for all nurses. Having a staff of nurses with education, family background and ideas similar to their own might be expected to help counter the increasingly militant labour mentality of nurses. When the profession reforms itself by systematizing its knowledge base, the ground is prepared for a very different approach to professional work. Simultaneously with the evolution, evaluation and widespread adoption of discourse-based methods of conceptualizing and teaching nursing, accountability practices which rely on just such innovations, have been introduced into Canadian hospitals. Nurses have wanted, as a minimum, to ensure competencies and confirm outcomes. A particular application of science makes this possible. However, in becoming a technique to be applied, documented and monitored, the administrative forms of 'the nursing process' lose some of their flexibility. In incorporating a management capacity into the conceptual framework for nursing, that focus for reform is carried into all aspects of the profession. A hint of the discomfort felt by nursing students whose experiences did not fit neatly into conceptual categories comes through in the literature on curriculum reform. This echoes my account, in the second section of this chapter, of similar disjunctures noted by practising nurses whose work was organized by objective management measures.

Objectivity and administration

Systematic frameworks help nurses to *order* their thinking through schemata which are useful in all manner of organizational activities.[56] Administrative control relies on such systematic information. Nurses, in making use of documentary management technologies, cannot assume that decisions are made in the interests either of them or of their patients, however. Control moves, along with objectively formated and, therefore, accountable information about nursing, into the hierarchies of the health-care system and the professions. Decision-makers, there, are committed, as part of the ruling apparatus, to making decisions in the best interests of the capitalist economy. Not only do front-line nurses lose control over their practice through objective determination of 'need' and of what constitutes 'quality', but administrative nurses at all levels lose some measure of control over their jurisdictions. Professional judgement can be bypassed when objective information is available to 'really', that is objectively, understand a situation. VanLoon[57] made a similar point in relation to what he saw as the decreasing role of health-care professionals *vis-à-vis* financial experts in the Canadian health-care system.

Decision-making in state organizations is based on criteria which express 'the common good'.[58] As White[59] indicates in discussing British nursing, what is good for the country, as politicians and/or bureaucrats see it, may not be good for nurses (or patients). 'The common good' is an expression which captures the sense of ruling objectives. 'Ruling', here, denotes the concerting of efforts towards objectives which promote dominant interests. In a liberal democracy, the method of determining a course of state action has been through promoting the public expression and debate of plural interests. The capacity of an increasingly integrated and technologically sophisticated ruling apparatus is more successfully to co-ordinate and concert otherwise divergent interests. Contemporary management and governing, as it is carried out in corporate organizations, is an increasingly objective practice. This chapter has been suggesting what this means as it is applied to hospitals and nurses.

In nursing management practices in hospitals, we have seen that decisions are made in conformity to objective rules and procedures, using criteria related to centrally determined priorities. Nurses are now being held, through *professional* commitments, as well as employment contracts, to documentary forms of action; the documents themselves are part of a structure of control tying nurses to political commitments, external to their practice, and outside their knowledge. In Canada, political decisions about social spending have targeted health-care expenditures for reduction, and hospital grants, especially, have been restricted. Under the new accounting processes for decision-making about practice, a contradiction arises between nurses' internalized values and the organizational (documentary) structuring and ordering of their actions. The impact on nurses of living with this contradiction has yet to be addressed adequately in the profession. The objective procedures actually write out and obliterate any traces of personally experienced responses. Canadian nursing unions address a range of membership problems including the professional responsibilities which nurses continue to carry after managerial practices divest them of much of the control over their work. Using this route to resist negative effects of management control over nursing practice is extremely cumbersome, however. It calls for nurses to develop alternative accounting systems, under union sponsorship. This route is also costly of nurses' time and of union support, although it has been shown to be effective in a number of 'safety-to-practice' issues.

There is a fundamental difficulty in using the collective bargaining system to address 'professional' issues, however. Unions play a role circumscribed by labour law and precedents in industrial, as opposed to professional, relations. The legal arena in which industrial relations are played out is not fully adequate to the task of rectifying the problems outlined in this chapter. A recent case in New Brunswick[60] provides a good example of this point. It shows how casting a nurse's problem into a legal decision-making framework creates a setting in which documents take precedence over arguments that nurses know how to make in experiential terms. Then the documentary reality, with its particular 'ruling' construction, becomes the officially sanctioned interpretation.

Some contextualizing information about the case highlights it as one in which extension of educational policy, representing 'the common good', sets up a contradiction in its individual and particular application. Organizing support for the new entry-to-practice policy has meant that, across the country, new educational requirements are being instituted for nursing positions *above the entry level*. A number of experienced and competent nurses, who lack university preparation, are having their careers arbitrarily truncated by the new minimum educational requirement which denies them promotion into headnurse positions. Until the effect of the new policy and its implementation plan began to be felt, nurses had been able to count on advancing in their careers by accumulating valued service and experience, through which they acquired increasing levels of competence. The new educational policy has resulted in a situation in which such nurses are having their competence questioned, as individuals, when they apply for promotion.

The New Brunswick Nurses' Union contested this and a number of similar employer decisions not to promote an otherwise qualified diploma nurse; the union questioned the new minimum educational requirement on the grounds that a university degree should not be considered the adequate and necessary indicator of a job applicant's competence. Under the collective agreement, any new requirement in a position description must be demonstrably a 'reasonable' one.[61] The union argued for 'equivalence' on the basis of experience, shifting the argument to the individual nurse's competence and how it was to be demonstrated. In the particular arbitration in question, the union's account of the nurse's competence included evidence that the hospital recognized it when she was asked to substitute in a supervisory position on numerous occasions; also, evidence was supplied that her co-workers saw her as the best person for the job, and a previous headnurse testified as to her capacity to do the work. The provincial Registered Nurses' Association, supported by the CNA, argued for the employer's position against its own nurse member. The objectivity of the position description and the value of the educational credential was argued (by the professional associations) to be the paramount arbiter of an applicant's suitability.

The professional association's 'Roles and Functions' position paper, prescribing proper levels of education, was entered as authoritative evidence of the reasonableness of the new requirement for a degree in the position description. The process by which the position paper had been prepared and through which it would be given formal status as Association policy was detailed in evidence, even though the profession's policy has no official status *vis-à-vis* hospital employment practices and collective agreements. The employer's decision was upheld. One observation which could be made about the process was that the arbitration hearing organized the decision-making process in relation to a legal apparatus in which documents from the profession came to stand in a privileged relation to other claims.

The CNA sees 'market forces' as both objectively organizing the demand for baccalaureate nurses in headnurse positions and appropriately taking care of the problem created.[62] The concept of 'market forces' detaches the professional associations from an agency role in the difficulties nurses are experiencing. The CNA policy, and its organizational campaign to influence opinion and gain support both inside and outside the profession, is disattended as an element in determining demand for baccalaureate nurses. The notion of 'market forces' means that the local availability of nurses with degrees (in any competition) determines whether or not a particular diploma nurse can be considered for promotion. Decisions about an individual's promotability, made through 'objective procedures' come, therefore, to have an arbitrary character.

The CNA's 'market forces' reaction to individual career and economic difficulties which their policy creates is, however, not the outcome of improper decisions or uncaring people. The association pursues those activities which lead most directly to 'the common good', as it has been established in policy. The association's response to individual cases reflects organizational priorities. The question of individual cases is treated objectively. As in the New Brunswick case, nurses with degrees meet the new requirements; those without, subject to availability of degreed nurses, do not, regardless of personal histories, accumulated competencies, and so on. The associations act only to secure what expresses 'the common good'. In this case, and others like it being argued across Canada, the profession is committed to keeping up the momentum towards universal university nursing education. Each case is a test of the strength that the profession has gained to reform itself and improve its status. Individual losses and suffering of individual members, arbitrariness, local needs and differences have no place in these decisions. The administrative method of knowing objectively lifts from its context in everyday experience only those attributes or features which match the profession's ruling preconceptualization. Likewise, the method frees the issue from 'personal' considerations.

Conclusions

By moving from research on information systems to some current issues surrounding nursing educational reform, I have suggested a 'framework for analysis' of current developments in nursing. Its major feature is the capacity for objective decision-making being incorporated into nursing theory, practice, education and organizations. My doctoral research explicated the social organization of the so-called 'hard data' about nursing, as it is generated and used within the health-care system. In it, I contrasted documentary knowledge of 'what was happening' in hospitals with nurses' own accounts of their contribution to developing those accounts. In many cases, the production of information in its proper formats took precedence over the primary function of nurses—caring for people; in every case, the production of information became the focus around which nurses' work was oriented. The information, its content, its conceptual structure, its inclusions and exclusions, was 'given' in the systematic ordering of record-keeping. The organizational consciousness of the health-care institution, and the entire health-care system, comes to have an 'engineered' character, thereby. Nurses are implicated, against their commitments to patients, in implementing budget cuts in their own practice. What I have described is not an aberration, but the contemporary method of knowing objectively, designed for efficient and effective management of an enterprise.

Nursing models postulate a nurse whose interests are those of a caring professional, orientated to her work as one intelligent and responsive individual interacting with another who has particular needs associated with his or her incapacities (through illness, life crises, hospitalization, etc.). A disjuncture exists between what nursing models postulate and the way management systems organize the work setting in which nurses act. Models are developed as 'ideal representations'; the organization abstracts from experienced reality of the work setting those particulars (which match ideal representations) which are needed to control its operation both in terms of the input of resources, and the (documen-tary) production of desired outcomes. The organization is operated by constructing and consulting a kind of idealized image of itself, to which its members must try to conform. Nurses struggle to maintain their own level of excellence under difficult conditions. They must structure their activities to conform to the information requirements, but also must respond to the day-to-day unreconstructed realities of hospital life.

In drawing analytic attention to the disjuncture between nursing ideals and nurses' experience, an educational policy issue is highlighted. Nursing theories and conceptual frameworks express the best intentions of the nursing profession, expressed as a set of ideas. Nursing instructors put their minds and energies into developing their students' capacities and attitudes in line with these frameworks. Nurses, working at all levels of practice, use their trained intelligence, their compassion and their practical skills in applying nursing knowledge. Between the conception and the actuality of nursing, textually mediated social organization interposes values and priorities which may differ from those of nurses. We might well ask if an educational programme should help nurses to understand their work as the product both of their trained contributions and of administrative imperatives imposed through new forms of document-based organization. Another question nurse educators should be considering is how much idealism or pragmatism is programmed into nursing frameworks now, and what effect this has on nurses' capacities to be flexible and effective in their jobs?

Another dilemma facing nursing is how to modernize nursing and prepare nurses for participating in corporate organizations while not devaluing knowledge which does not fit into objective frameworks. The feminist movement has noted that women have developed and exercise important skills and knowledge, in their mothering and caring work, isolated from the 'public sphere'; these are too valuable to the human species to lose, even though we may not want to assign women, consistently, to conventional gender-related work roles. The point to be made is that the social organization of contemporary capitalism is antithetical to some very desirable human characteristics.[63] The feminist revolution is not aimed at replacing womanly capacities and expertise, but at organizing proper recognition and value for women's work. Neither should nursing, while in the first flush of organizing itself on a scientific and rational basis, lose touch with its traditional feminine attributes.

Textually mediated social organization provides, in the society in which we live, for the co-ordinated and orderly governing and management of social life. Nurses and nursing could not, even if they wished, step outside contemporary social organization. They participate and learn to adopt modern methods, as a condition of being part of a dynamic society, dedicated, as ours is, to growth and efficiency, as well as to liberal principles. Along with the benefits of advances in organizational practice, which are many, are some systematically undesirable effects. Until untoward effects of administrative reform are chronicled, and legitimated by research which shows their social character, they remain personal problems with individual solutions. I am not alone in drawing attention to these related problems,[64] although a commitment from the profession to be open and responsive to them awaits research which makes their social organization visible. The challenge still facing nursing is how to be instrumental in shaping its present and future practice, as opposed to adapting nursing practice to techniques which are part of the corporatization of the public health-care system.

References

1. Campbell, Marie L., *Information Systems and Management of Hospital Nursing: A Study in Social Organization of Knowledge.* PhD dissertation, Department of Sociology in Education, OISE, University of Toronto, 1984.
2. Smith, Dorothy E., 'Textually mediated social organization', *International Social Science Journal*, 1984, **36**, No. 1, 59–75.
3. See reference 2, p. 62.
4. See reference 2, p. 61.
5. Spender, Dale, *Man Made Language.* Routledge & Kegan Paul, London, 1980.
6. For example Hardy, Leslie, 'Career politics: the case of career histories of selected leading female and male nurses in England and Scotland'. In White, R. (ed.), *Political Issues in Nursing*, vol. II, John Wiley, Chichester, 1986, pp. 69–82.
7. Smith, Dorothy E., 'Women's perspective as a radical critique of sociology', *Sociological Inquiry*, 1974, **44**, No. 1, 7–13.
8. See reference 7, p. 9.
9. See reference 7, p. 11.
10. Research in Canadian nursing is still a new field; see *The Development of Nursing Research in Canada*, prepared by the Nursing Research Committee of the Canadian Nurses' Association, September 1981.
11. See reference 1.
12. See reference 1, Chapters 4, 5 and 6.
13. Reports of Canadian publicly funded Research and Development of patient classification systems include MacDonell, J. A. K. and Murray, G. B., 'An Index of Care', *Medical Services Journal Canada*, 1965, **21**, No. 8 (September), 499–517; Holmlund, B. A., *Nursing Study Phase 1, University Hospital*, University of Saskatchewan, Hospital Systems Study Group, 1967; Giovannetti, Phyllis and McKague, Laverne, *Patient Classification System and Staffing by Workload Index: A Working Manual.* Saskatoon, Hospital Systems Study Group, 1973; Equipe de Recherche Operationnelle en Santé, *PRN 76: An Information System for Nursing Management*, Dept. d'Administration de la Santé, Universite de Montreal, 1978 (a users' guide in three booklets).

14. Increasingly sophisticated Quality Assurance systems have been developed by consulting firms specializing in nursing management which are now being hired to implement objective controls in (large, urban) hospital nursing departments. For example, an integrated Patient Classification and Quality Assurance system has been implemented by Medicus Systems Corporation in the University of Alberta Hospitals, Edmonton.
15. Little, Delores and Carnevali, Doris, *Nursing Care Planning*, 2nd edition. Lippincott, Philadelphia, 1976, p. 11.
16. Mitchell, Pamela, 'The process of diagnosis', *Concepts Basic to Nursing*. McGraw-Hill, New York, 1977, pp. 81–116.
17. See reference 15.
18. Roberts, Carolyn and Yaros, Patricia, 'Theoretical pluralism and curriculum design'. In McGee, M. (ed.), *Theoretical Pluralism in Nursing Science*. University of Ottawa Press, Ottawa, 1984, pp. 112–113.
19. See reference 18, pp. 106–109.
20. See reference 1, p. 143.
21. See Campbell, Marie, 'The structure of stress in nurses' work', forthcoming in Bolaria, S. and Dickinson, H. (eds), *Sociology of Health and Health Care in Canada*. Harcourt Brace Jovanovich, Canada, Don Mills, 1988, for a detailed explication of how the conflation occurs.
22. Regulation 449, Revised Regulations of Ontario, 1980, as amended to O.Reg., 144/85 under the Health Disciplines Act (Nursing), January 1986.
23. Ontario, Health Disciplines Act (Nursing), Section 73 (f).
24. College of Nurses of Ontario, *Standards of Nursing Practice: for Registered Nurses and Nursing Assistants*, Toronto, 1976, revised, 1979 and 1983.
25. But see Baumgart, Alice, 'The conflicting demands of professionalism and trade unionism', *International Nursing Review*, 1983, **30**, No. 5, 150–155.
26. Campbell, Marie L., 'Management as ruling: a class phenomenon in nursing', unpublished ms., 1986.
27. Campbell, Marie L., 'Productivity in Canadian Nursing: administering cuts'. In Coburn, D., D'Arcy, C., Torrance, G. and New, P. (eds), *Health and Canadian Society*. Fitzhenry and Whiteside, Toronto, 1987, pp. 463–475.
28. Statistics Canada, *1981 Census of Canada: Population*, Catalogue 71-202S, Ottawa, 1984.
29. Canadian Nurses' Association, *Entry to Practice Newsletter*, 1985, **1**, No. 15 (July).
30. Collective Agreement Binding the Alberta Hospital Association and the United Nurses of Alberta for the period 1 January 1984–31 December 1985, Salaries Appendix, p. 75.
31. Baumgart, Alice, 'Unionism and the professional employee: the experience of Canadian Registered Nurses in negotiating professional responsibility clauses', presented at the Canadian–American Health Management Conference, Montreal, 1980.
32. See, for example, Article 36, 'Professional Responsibility' in the United Nurses of Alberta Collective agreement, 1984–1985.
33. But see the fourth section of this chapter for a discussion of the difficulties faced in playing this role.
34. Baumgart, Alice, *Sixty Plus Years of University Nursing Education in*

Canada. Paper presented at the meetings of CAUSN, Learned Societies' Conference, Dalhousie University, Halifax, June 1981.

35. See reference 34, p. 10.
36. McFarlane, Elizabeth, 'Nursing theory: the comparison of four theoretical proposals', *Journal of Advanced Nursing*, 1980, **5**, 3–19.
37. Canadian Nurses' Association, *Entry to Practice Newsletter*, 1984, **1**, No. 9 (December).
38. Minutes of the Canadian Nurses' Association Board of Directors' meeting, 26–28 October 1983.
39. See reference 37.
40. See CAUSN Position Paper on Entry Level Preparation for Nursing Practice, 1980, especially p. 2.
41. Canadian Nurses' Association, *The Expanded Role of the Nurse: Working Paper*, by R. Lamothe, Ottawa, 1972.
42. Canadian Nurses' Association, Brief to the House of Commons Standing Committee on Health, Welfare and Social Affairs in Response to the Proposed Canada Health Act, 1984, p. 19.
43. Alford, Robert, *Health Care Politics*. University of Chicago Press, Chicago, 1975, p. 15.
44. For more on community-based health care, particularly 'Barriers and obstacles' to widespread implementation, see Canadian Council on Social Development, *Community-based Health and Social Services*, Proceedings of the Ottawa Conference, 24–27 November 1985.
45. See Bullock, A. and Campbell, M., 'Community care: gendered, ideology-bound, ruling practices'. Paper presented at the Canadian Sociology and Anthropology Association Meetings, Learned Societies' Conference, University of Manitoba, Winnipeg, 1986.
46. Attridge, Carolyn, 'Curriculum iatrogenesis (side effects)'. In McGee, M. (ed.), *Theoretical Pluralism in Nursing Science*. University of Ottawa Press, Ottawa, 1984, pp. 119–134.
47. See reference 46, pp. 132–133.
48. Minutes of ORCAUSN Council 5 October 1975; 20 February 1976, held in the Queen's University Archives, Kingston, Ontario.
49. See Silva, Mary and Rothbart, Daniel, 'An analysis of changing trends in philosophies of science on nursing theory development and testing', *Advances in Nursing Science*, 1984, **6**, No. 2, 1–13, for a critical review of the foundations of nursing 'science'.
50. Secretary of State, Canada, *Accessibility to Postsecondary Education in Canada*, by P. Anisef, Ottawa: Education Support Branch, 1985.
51. Canadian Federation of Students, *An Educational Mortgage: Student Aid in 1986, Part One*, by J. Wright, Ottawa: Canadian Federation of Students, 1986.
52. Statistics Canada, '1981 Census of Canada: Population', Ottawa, May 1984.
53. See reference 52.
54. See reference 29.
55. See reference 29.
56. See also Robinson, Jane, 'Health visiting and health'. In White, R. (ed.), *Political Issues in Nursing: Past, Present and Future*, vol. 1, John Wiley, Chichester, 1985, p. 81.

57. VanLoon, R., 'From shared cost to block funding and beyond: the politics of health insurance in Canada', *Journal of Health Politics, Policy and Law*, 1978, 454–477.
58. White, Rosemary, 'Political regulators in British nursing'. In White, R. (ed.), *Political Issues in Nursing: Past, Present and Future*, vol. 1, John Wiley, Chichester, 1985, pp. 19–43.
59. See reference 58, pp. 35–37.
60. A grievance filed by the New Brunswick Nurses' Union over a decision by the administration of Hotel Dieu de Tracadie Hospital not to promote Paulette Doiron resulted in a grievance arbitration heard by Dr Noel Kinsella, 15 September 1986.
61. I am grateful to Mary Jane Richards, Labour Relations Officer, New Brunswick Nurses' Union, for explaining the legal basis on which this case was argued.
62. Personal communication from M. Lamb, Director of Personnel Services, Canadian Nurses' Association.
63. See Ferguson, Kathy, *The Feminist Case Against Bureaucracy*. Temple University Press, Philadelphia, 1984.
64. See, for instance, Jennifer Craig's critique of nursing models in 'Viewpoint', *RNABC News*, 1986, **18**, No. 5, 23–27; or, a popular account of the problems nurses face by Lipovenko, D., 'Hospitals alarmed as disgruntled nurses flee the profession' in *The Globe and Mail*, National Edition, 6 December 1986, p. A4.

Political Issues in Nursing: Past, Present and Future, Volume 3
Edited by R. White
© 1988 John Wiley & Sons Ltd

CHAPTER 5

Dependency matters: an issue in the care of elderly people

JILLIAN M. MacGUIRE, BA, PhD, RGN
Research and Development Officer, Elderly Care Unit, Mid-Staffordshire Health Authority, Stafford, England

Introduction

The association of age and dependency is no longer seen as axiomatic. Biological ageing and chronological age do not necessarily go hand in hand. Recent research on the biological aspects of ageing shows that much of the loss in functional ability which has been regarded as inevitable may be postponed.[1] Pressure groups working on behalf of older people and the elderly themselves argue that people can continue to lead healthy and active lives into their 80s and 90s.[2] Ageism, like racism and sexism, is the subject of research and a target of criticism.[3] Townsend has argued forcefully that the dependency of the elderly is a creation of social policy during the twentieth century.[4] Dependency is manufactured and structured by social and economic forces 'which govern the position which the elderly occupy in national life, and these also contribute powerfully to the public consciousness of different meanings of ageing and old age'.[5] Physical and mental frailty, coupled with poverty and homelessness, have been used and are still being used to legitimate the placement of a proportion of elderly people in institutions. However benevolent the dispensation, entry into long-term care involves a loss of self and an erosion of civil liberties.[6]

Research on life in institutional settings from Goffman[7] to Phillipson, Bernard and Strang[8] suggests that the dependency of populations in geriatric and psychiatric hospitals, local authority homes, private nursing homes and residential homes is not simply a reflection of the impairment in functional capacity of the individuals. Measured dependency is also a product of institutionalization; the outcome of the specific regimes under which elderly people are cared for within those institutions. The dependency characteristics of individuals, moreover, are an insufficient explanation for admission to institutional life.[9] Individuals with similar dependency characteristics may be found in the community and in hospitals and homes. Low-dependency patients are found in geriatric wards while high-dependency residents may be living in sheltered accommodation. Yet dependency is one of the major *stated* criteria for admission to institutional care and the basis on which decisions are made, or supposed to be made, about the appropriateness of particular forms of care.[10]

Lester and Baltes,[11] Miller[12] and Evers[13] among others have implicated nurses as being primary actors in the creation and maintenance of dependency. Care staff also collude in the production of dependency.[14] What Auden actually wrote was that 'The *friends* of the born nurse are always getting worse'.[15] This seems to be the case also for their patients. Such dependency is the product of the interaction between residents and staff. Perceptions of elderly people as being 'like children' and the use of pet names and forenames, even with apparent agreement,[16] serve to emphasize the marginal status of residents and patients.

While geriatricians stress the importance and value of the rehabilitative aspects of care[17] the traditional medical model is still alive and well in many geriatric wards and nursing homes where the emphasis is on physical tasks rather than on the social aspects of care.[18] 'Warehousing' is the unattractive yet apposite term that has been applied to this model of care.[19] Dual registration is being resisted by some pressure groups in the private residential homes sector, ostensibly because of the fear that the medical model and a clinical approach to care will be imported along with the nurses.[20]

Much of the work currently being carried out on patient dependency in hospitals is related to the setting of establishments,[21] the measuring of workloads[22] and the allocation of nursing resources within units.[23] Nurses in some geriatric units are using dependency measures at ward level to record and monitor the progress, or in some cases lack of progress, of patients towards the goal of independence. Such records may be used to demonstrate the effect of nursing intervention on patient outcomes.[24]

Major shifts in the definition of old' age are taking place. As the number of elderly in the population has gone up the definition of the age at which people become the official concern of social policy has risen *pari passu*. As late as 1971 Harris[25] took the starting point to be 60 for women and 65 for men. Women make up a disproportionate number of those who survive into old age and the consideration of women between 60 and 65 as 'old' is regarded as old-fashioned if not an expression of ageism. The Audit Commission confines itself to those aged 75 and over[26] with the 'elderly elderly' or those aged 85 and over being seen as the subject of primary concern. Those aged 95 and over have been identified as a group requiring special provisions in hospital and in the community.[27]

It may be that there has been such a marked improvement in the health of elderly people and a concomitant reduction in the proportion of disabled in the 'younger elderly' group that such a postponement of entry into official old age is justified. The relationship between age and relative poverty and between poverty and health detailed in the Black Report[28] might lead one to question the extent of such progress.

It is tempting to suggest that we are witnessing a restructuring of reality akin to the changes in the bases for redefining the unemployed. Remove a decade from the figures and the rates of provision per thousand of the age group appear more generous and comparisons with past levels of provision are more difficult to make. The proportion of people aged 65 and over in institutional care declined between 1911 and 1981.[29] Geriatric beds declined in the decade 1974–84 and though there was some increase in local authority provision between 1974 and 1979 the rate of provision per thousand has gone down sharply as the total number of people in the age group has gone up.[30] Numbers of beds in private nursing homes occupied by elderly people have doubled, while places in private residential homes have tripled, bringing the rate from 7.8 per thousand aged 75 and over in 1974 to 17.4 per thousand in 1984. Rates for domiciliary services, apart from day centre places, have remained static. Thus we have the paradox of policies for the elderly which continue to advocate community care,[31] static domiciliary provision and an increase in institutional care in the *private* sector sufficient to more than offset the decline in NHS geriatric beds. The downward trend in institutional provision appears to have been halted if not actually reversed. The explosion in numbers of beds in private residential homes looks set to be matched by an equivalent increase in private nursing home beds occupied by the elderly.[32]

The expansion of places in residential homes and nursing homes is a direct consequence of the financing of individual residents and patients through the supplementary benefit system.[33] It is clear that both district health authorities and local authorities have reached a plateau in the provision of beds and are now looking covertly or overtly to the private sector to provide at least part of the shortfall from a different compartment of the public purse. The Audit Commission[34] and the Labour Party[35] have given notice of intent to curb this development and rechannel the resources into community care.

Some health authorities are closing long-term geriatric beds as nursing-home beds become available. While a number of authorities have introduced procedures which aim at cutting out the unscrupulous and non-viable potential home owner, none has set any ceiling on the number of places per 1000 aged 75 and over which they are prepared to accept. It does not appear that existing legislation gives authorities the right to refuse registration on the grounds that too many homes with too many places are being set up within their boundaries.

A major but as yet largely uncharted development in the private sector is the introduction of dual registration whereby a single home may offer both 'residential' and 'nursing' care. 'An important objective of dual registration is that there need be no physical transfer from one home to another when a resident's condition changes.'[36] This change has been widely welcomed. In practice, the regulations which give the designated senior nurse of a district health authority the right to demand that a residential home become dually registered or that a resident be moved into a nursing home may further 'erode the rights of individual residents who can be moved against their own wishes, those of their relatives, their doctors and the proprietor of their home'.[37] The NAHA guidelines imply that the distinction between a resident and someone requiring nursing care turns upon the extent of the dependency of the individual in question.[38] The guidelines do not, however, suggest how such dependency might be measured.

The measurement of dependency

Dependency is thus a key concept in policy issues related to the elderly. The British Society of Gerontology devoted its 1985 Annual Conference to a wide range of papers on aspects of dependency.[39] The concept is used in a number of discrete but interconnected ways

(1) Structural dependency: concerned with the way in which the role and position of the elderly population as a whole is defined. The

extent of the relative deprivation and rates of institutionalization of the elderly are possible measures of such dependency.

(2) Institutional dependency: concerned with the way in which living in institutions such as prisons, hospitals or residential homes restricts personal rights, choices and activities. Institutional dependency underpins and reinforces structural dependency and creates the settings in which people who share the same dependency characteristics as those in sheltered accommodation or living unsupported in the community may become dependent on others in all aspects of their daily life. Possible measures of such dependency would involve looking at how free residents are to determine the time they get up and go to bed, whether they have choices at meal times, whether they are free to enter their rooms at any time in the day or to leave the home to go to church, the shops or the pub. Bergman[40] has suggested six domains, physical environment, psycho-social environment, basic personal care, health care, family involvement and manpower, in which all services for the elderly should be assessed and has developed a standard measurement schedule for the evaluation of quality of care.

(3) Dependency characteristics: concerned with the degree of impairment or the extent of loss of function. A wide range of items, including age itself, may be considered such as restricted mobility, difficulties with washing and dressing, problems with eating, incontinence, impairment of speech, hearing or sight, confusion and various other potentially disabling conditions. Measures include the distribution of such characteristics within and between defined populations of elderly people. Differences between different types of institution, between institutional and non-institutional populations and differences over time within a single type of institution may be explored. Assessment procedures, the appropriateness of placement and the equity of resource allocation may be investigated.

(4) Interactive dependency: concerned with the expression of the *relationship* between an individual elderly person and an individual carer whether that person be relative, care assistant or nurse. Here dependency is seen not as an attribute of the individual but as the product of the interaction between two people. A person may be disabled, impaired or handicapped in isolation, and measures of disability exist,[41] may have dependency needs which are not being met[42] but can only be *dependent* in relation

to someone else whether actual or implied. Measurement involves the assessment of the needs or requirements of the individual for care, coupled with the recording or estimation of the time and the expertise required of the carer. Notions of care goals and standards of care are also involved.

Barr introduced the concept of patient dependency to nursing in this country in the 1960s[43] as a surrogate workload index. His interest was primarily with patients in acute hospital wards and was one of the first attempts to create a rational basis for setting ward establishments. His approach was further developed by Mulligan.[44]

Classification systems or typologies have proliferated. Within nursing, classifications have been devised by Barr,[45] Norwich,[46] Rhys-Hearn,[47] Wade and Snaith,[48] Cheltenham and District Health Authority,[49] Mid-Staffordshire Health Authority,[50] North Western Regional Health Authority,[51] Northern Regional Health Authority,[52] Leicestershire Health Authority,[53] the Scottish Home and Health Department,[54] as a basis for CASH,[55] and by Senior.[56] Some of these were reviewed by Wilson-Barnett in 1978[57] and the details of several are set out in a DHSS document on estimating workloads published in 1984.[58]

The spread in the use of *Monitor*[59] suggests that this classification may become one which is generally acceptable. While there may be some merit in devising new systems for particular specialities where no such system already exists, a great deal of effort up and down the country does seem to be going into devising classifications in areas such as geriatrics where there are already a number of widely used measures.

Similar classification systems have been developed for use in residential settings. A WHO publication of 1984 reviews multi-disciplinary assessments.[60] The main focus has been on the exploration of differences between homes of the same kind and between populations in different kinds of residential care. Elderly people in long-stay geriatric wards have frequently been included in such studies. The classification developed by Wade, based on that of Rhys-Hearn, called The Elderly Person Dependency Form (EPDF) has been used by her and others to look at the distribution of elderly people in six different settings, including hospitals. In order to apply the measure they have made the assumption that the 'rank order of nursing dependency does not differ in different contexts' and point out that this assumption would have to be made whatever method of assessment were used.[61] Other systems have also been used in this type of multi-disciplinary study. Macdonal *et al*.[62] have looked at elderly people in four different settings in London;

Atkinson, Bond and Gregson[63] have compared the dependency characteristics of older people in five forms of institutional care; Booth[64] has looked at changes in dependency among a cohort of 3412 residents in 175 local authority homes; and Coles[65] has looked at dependency in local authority homes in the Durham area. Different classificatory systems have been used in these studies but broad comparisons may be made between them.

The principle is the same whatever the specifics of the classification. Any population of patients in hospital or nursing home, residents in private homes or in local authority homes, people in sheltered housing or the elderly in their own homes may be grouped according to how much support they need from nursing staff, care staff or relatives.

The uses of dependency

Most of the dependency classifications used in hospital settings have been developed as a basis for determining nurse staffing establishments. The precise way in which dependency data are converted into workload indices and workload indices grossed up to produce establishment figures is outside the scope of this chapter. The methodology for calculating establishments continues to be the subject of criticism but this does not invalidate the use of patient dependency measures as such. In reviewing dependency-based methods the DHSS study team stated that the 'major advantages of all dependency-based methods considered here are their explicit assessment of workload related to the dependency of the patient and the use of uniform, explicitly defined standards of care in terms of quality or frequency of various tasks'.[66] Many dependency-based systems have the added advantage that they can form part of information systems for defining objectives for individual patient care, monitoring progress, monitoring staffing levels and aiding nurse managers to deploy their available staff to meet short-term fluctuations in workload.

The systems have many features in common. Table 1 details the items included in some of the more widely used published scales. Items which recur are washing, dressing, feeding, mobility and incontinence. Criteria for the assessment of each individual under each item are also laid down. There is, as might be expected if these systems have any validity, a measure of agreement on the descriptive terms used to discriminate between patients as the examples in Table 2 demonstrate. Whether the assessment of patient dependency is done over a short period to establish ward-dependency profiles, or is integrated into the ongoing ward

Table 1   Patient dependency classifications

Items	Classification				
	Chelt (1)	N West (2)	KTC (3)	Barr (4)	Rhys-Hearn (5)
Washing	X	}X	X	}X	X
Dressing	X	}	X	}	X
Feeding	X	X	X	X	X
Continence	X	X	X		X
Mobility	X	X	X	X	X
Pressure areas			X		
Mental awareness				X	X
Psychological needs	X				
Social needs	X				
Nursing attention		X		X	
Prescribed treatment				X	
Other		X			
Number of items	7	6	6	6	6+3

(1) Cheltenham and District Health Authority (ref. 49)
(2) North West Staffing Project Criteria for Care (ref. 51)
(3) Mid-Staffordshire Health Authority (ref. 50)
(4) Mulligan, B. (ref. 44)
(5) Wade and Snaith (ref. 48) Six items are shown on the table. The others are consciousness, toileting and ability to benefit from instruction.

information, training is and must be given to researchers and ward staff on how to fill in the forms. Refresher courses as well as initial training are necessary if the use of dependency ratings becomes part of day-to-day ward recording. All systems have in common a method for converting the ratings on each item into an overall score or dependency category. It is a short step then to calculate the number and percentage of patients falling into each of the dependency groups within a ward. Where the system is in continuous use, weekly, monthly and yearly summaries can be produced for each ward, unit or hospital if required. Comparative data from three different systems are shown in Table 3. Such summaries give nursing managers and ward sisters a more accurate picture of the population of patients being treated within a ward area. Staff views that a ward is 'getting heavier' can be explored with some measure of objectivity and assertions that 'Ward A is lighter than Ward B though Ward B has fewer staff' can be tested. Other things being equal, the expectation is that the weekly, monthly and yearly patterns for wards will fluctuate about the mean. Changes in admission policies, changes in medical and nursing practices and modifications in discharge policies can markedly affect the distribution of patients between dependency groups, reflecting an increase or decrease in the workload. The effect of such changes can be monitored if not even anticipated. In long-stay areas, where the number of discharges is low, the dependency totals are likely to creep up over time. Unless this is monitored existing nursing staff may be expected simply to absorb the additional workload. The question of whether patients are slowly deteriorating over time or whether staff are taking a non-rehabilitative approach may also be explored. Continuous data sets may show up unanticipated seasonal fluctuations.

Table 2

Cheltenham and District Health Authority: Patient Categorizing Form (see ref. 49)

Points awarded	**Mobility**
1	Independent
2	One-nurse assistance
3	Two-nurse assistance
4	Bed/chairfast

Criteria for Care: North West Staffing Project (see ref. 51)

	Mobility
A	Up and about
B	Bed rest/up with help
C	Bed/chair with position/support

KTC Standard Dependency Groups: Mid Staffordshire (see ref. 50)

	Mobility
1	Self-sufficient
2	Requires one nurse
3	Requires 2 nurses
4	Confused hyperactive bed rest and/or sitting out for short periods

NB Layout has been rearranged to point up similarities.

The working group on staff mix found few geriatric wards where dependency data were routinely collected.[67] Many nurses seem unaware of the existence of dependency classification systems unless they happen to work in an area where such systems have been introduced. They are seen by some as a management or research tool which has little to offer them. Classifying or grouping of patients may also be regarded as running counter to the principle that every patient is unique and care must be tailored to meet his specific requirements. Filling in forms is viewed as another chore which takes up time that would otherwise be devoted to direct patient care. Others have taken the idea on board at a personal level and are quick to see ways in which the approach may be used to enhance patient care.

Table 3

Cheltenham		Category		
	High			Low
(See ref. 49, example derived from p. 69)	4	3	2	1
Totals for month	31	155	435	217
Daily average	1.0	5.0	14.0	7.0
% in category	3.7	18.5	51.9	25.9

North West		Category		
	High			Low
(See ref. 51, example taken from p. 128)	I	II	III	IV
Totals for month	96	303	86	25
Daily average	3.1	9.8	2.8	0.8
% in category	18.8	59.4	17.0	4.8

Mid-Staffordshire		Dependency group		
	High			Low
(unpublished data)	A	B	C	D
Total for month	288	287	79	57
Daily average	9.3	12.3	2.5	1.8
% per group	35.5	47.7	9.8	7.0

There are very real problems about who is going to handle the material and feed information back both to management and ward levels. Without the appointment of someone with specific responsibility for this aspect of the work it is difficult to envisage that the data will do anything but fill up filing cabinets. While most systems are simple enough for hand analysis, the task is made much easier if computer facilities are available. The appointment of nurse researchers at unit level may help to spread the use of *Monitor* and *Criteria for Care* and, with them, the use of dependency classifications.

What are the implications, if any, for direct patient care of the use of dependency information? Most of the systems described make use of aggregated patient data but all systems lend themselves to the keeping of a daily, weekly or monthly record for individual patients. A dependency rating on admission gives an invaluable base-line against which the extent of deterioration or improvement may be measured. The fact that all items are structured on a continuum from 'assistance required' to 'independent' or 'self-caring' reinforces the goal-orientated aspects of nursing care and, particularly in the context of the care of the elderly, stresses the importance attached to rehabilitation. Looking at the record (see Table 3) in conjunction with the care plan, should help to prevent nurses jumping in and doing for a patient what he can already demonstrably do for himself. Where wards are arranged in dependent and independent bays, experience in the use of the rating system will suggest a score above which an individual patient should not be moved to a self-care area. The same principle holds true where the practice is that a whole ward is designated as an 'independent' or a 'rehabilitation' ward. Such decisions may involve ward sisters and nursing management in confrontation with medical staff who may seek to move patients to independent bays or wards or even to discharge patients at too high a dependency level in order to facilitate admissions. The pressure to reduce the length of stay and increase the throughput of patients extends to the elderly. Dependency data do suggest that there are peak discharge times for individuals and that their dependency *increases* if they are not discharged. But the consequences of discharging patients before that time in terms of readmission rates and residual disability may be much more serious than for younger patients. Revolving door patients do not indicate cost effectiveness in care. The dependency score does give a way of assessing whether a patient is suitable for transfer or ready for discharge and can provide a useful adjunct to the professional opinion of those involved in the negotiations about transfer and discharge.

A sister may also argue that the workload represented by her patients is already high and that further admissions to empty beds would increase that workload to unsafe levels. Though she is within her rights and duty in the terms of the UKCC Code of Professional Practice[68] and should be supported by her nursing manager, the ripple effects of taking up such a position may extend beyond the unit in which she works and be seen as politically unacceptable by managers of larger and more powerful units. Geriatric wards are not well-staffed and show more variation from ward to ward than can be explained by reference to the dependency of their patients.[69]

Some district health authorities are using dependency data in a systematic way to look at differences in workload between wards and to reallocate nurse staffing accordingly. But even where there is a uniform approach within one authority the political will and political power may not actually exist to bring about any transfer of resources between low-dependency and high-dependency areas. The staffing of psycho-geriatric wards, where patients may also be physically disabled as a result of a stroke or some other intercurrent condition, in accordance with the requirements of a dependency reallocation formula would involve a major shift in the distribution of nursing manpower. Equity in nursing care for elderly people in hospital is not yet a reality.

If dependency assessments at ward and unit level are to feed into overall manpower decisions it is imperative not only that a standard dependency measure is used in all wards and departments but that the chief nurse advisor to the authority has some say in the setting and annual review of nursing establishments. Without that necessary involvement, the establishments which were in force at the time of the Griffiths implementation[70] will tend to be perpetuated in so far as they are not whittled down by purely financial considerations.

This use of dependency classifications is growing and it is a development to be welcomed by nurses not only in the search for equity in resource allocation between patients in different sectors but also as a tool to assist manpower planning in general. Quality of care also hinges on the appropriateness of staffing levels in relation to workloads as measured by dependency. The relationships between dependency, staffing levels, staff mix, quality of care, cost and patient outcomes have by no means been fully elucidated. Despite the recantation of Barr and Moores[71] many researchers and most practitioners do consider that the *patients* in the beds, and not just the number of staffed, occupied beds, matter.

Monitoring dependency at the individual patient level opens up all kinds of interesting avenues of enquiry of the sort that are being pursued in relation to residential and long-stay care. For example, is the measured dependency of patients in different wards a reflection of differences in the *initial* dependency of the patients admitted or is it a product of the care regime including the number and grade of the staff employed? Fundamentally this is a question about quality of care and has to be asked and answered not just at some general level but specifically at the individual ward level. Given that the patients admitted to a number of wards are similar in terms of their dependency and other characteristics, including their medical condition, do wards rehabilitate people at different rates and to different degrees and if so why? Is it, as suggested in *Mix and Match*,[72] to do with the leadership offered by the ward sister or is it to do, as Wade, Sawyer and Bell postulate,[73] with the model of care adopted either explicitly or implicitly by the nursing staff?

Models of Care

Nursing models tend, as might be expected, to focus on the interaction between individual nurse and individual patient. The Roper model[74] is probably the most widely used in hospitals and the most taught in schools of nursing in this country with its emphasis on problem identification, goal-setting, problem-solving and evaluation. In many respects the Orem model[75] is more appropriate to the care of the elderly with its emphasis on the balance between the care giver and the individual and on the interactive nature of the caring relationship. This model, with its concepts of dependency needs and self-care deficits, sits comfortably with the use of dependency measures as a way of measuring patient progress. Together they provide an antidote to the creation of dependency.

The social context in which this personal care is taking place is not seen as problematic within the Roper model. In acute settings where the in-patient stay is very short this may not matter too much even in the case of elderly people.[76] In the longer term care of the elderly it is crucial. Wade and Snaith described four models of care which they found in the homes which they investigated.[77] The regimes in the homes could be conceptualized along two dimensions, person-centred versus task-centred and open versus closed, giving rise to four different models of care. These were classified as supportive, controlled, protective or restrained. The supportive model of care is characterized by the involvement of the elderly in decisions and by emphasis on physical and mental independence. In the controlled model the patient is subordinated to the care regime, diversional activities are provided and motivation comes from the staff. The protective model is characterized by some degree of choice but there is a strong emphasis on safety which circumscribes the activities of residents and thus denies them adult status. The restrained model of care operates purely for the convenience of care staff. Wade used the term 'batch processed' to describe the care in this last setting. Both the protected and the restrained model are likely to produce dependency. In the first situation patients or residents are confirmed in their dependent status by not being allowed to do things which might put them at risk. This can encompass anything from leaving the home unescorted to carrying a cup of tea. The restrained model creates dependency through the routinization of daily life and through the organization of everything from the time people get up to the range of meals provided on the basis of what is most convenient for the staff. Evers's 'patient career' groups are created within the restrained model.[78] Dependency can be confirmed, increased and promoted in some settings; reduced, resisted and forestalled in others.

At the social policy level the 'progressive dependency' model has been overtaken not only by a change in ideas but also by events. The progressive dependency model, analogous to the idea of progressive patient care only in reverse, involves the idea of a *range* of institutional settings, from those catering for people with minimal support requirements to those providing for people with high-dependency needs. Within this model individuals can, will and should move between these settings as their dependency increases.

Research shows that individuals do not move in any ordered way between their own homes, sheltered accommodation, local authority or residential care and continuing care in the NHS or private nursing homes. A high proportion of admissions to any form of residential care are crisis admissions and the availability of a bed in a particular home frequently outweighs the consideration of whether that might be the most appropriate for that individual. Many major decisions about where elderly people spend their *dependent* years appear to be made without full knowledge, assessment of and access to these alternatives.[79] Such options are by no means neutral financially either at the personal, local or central level. Continuing care in geriatric wards is an open-ended commitment and though attempts are made in some wards to rehabilitate patients, and a minority do move out into supported settings, many are likely to remain in hospital until they die. Although supplementary benefit is stopped on admission and state pensions reduced after eight weeks in hospital, patients and relatives do not have to give up the home and possessions of the patient. Sometimes property is sold up while patients are in hospital thus rendering them *homeless* and preventing discharge *home*. Admission to other forms of institutional care often involves selling up home and possessions as part of the deal whereby the elderly are given state support for as many years as they survive. Even should their level of independence be improved by the quality of the care given in the home the option to move back into their own home, supported by community services, has been irrevocably lost. There is some movement between different types of home, but once a move into residential care has been made the move back into *community* care is not easy in practice.

The progressive dependency model is linked to the *progressive cost* model which demonstrates increasing costs for an individual of a given level as you move from the domiciliary setting to the NHS setting. The Audit Commission gives an example at 1986 prices of £97.35 per week at home with domicilary care and £294.75 in an NHS hospital bed for a frail elderly single person.

> Clearly, the cost of inappropriate placement is significant. Recent studies and audits have shown that people are placed in residential care who are not as dependent. . . . Under these circumstances, such people are receiving more care than they need, undermining independence and increasing costs.[80]

A similar view is taken by many consultants, who see such inappropriate placement as the root cause of the blocking of acute and long-term geriatric beds.

The majority of residents in private nursing[81] and residential homes[82] pay their own fees and there are many reasons other than just dependency which have brought about their admission. One of these may well be difficulty in getting adequate support in the community. The refusal of state support to the small minority among those in residential care who are deemed to be insufficiently dependent will hardly provide the necessary cash injection for a sustained expansion of community provisions.

What is needed is a radical change in the model of financing care for elderly people which takes into account the changes which are currently taking place in the actual type and level of care which is being given in different settings in spite of the formal financing and registration arrangements. An income support system is required which makes it easier for elderly people to pay for what they need, whether they choose to live in a nursing home, residential setting, sheltered housing or to remain in their own homes. Doctrinaire views about it being better for people to remain in the community should not be used to justify withdrawal of support for the minority who want to take up the option of residential or nursing care but who cannot afford to do so.

Though nursing and residential homes may be officially classed as *institutional* care and local authorities regard residential care as undermining the philosophy of community care, many of those who own and manage homes see them as part of *community* care and health authorities see both as important resources in enabling the discharge of dependent patients back into the community.

Repeated studies of elderly people demonstrate that individuals of all dependency levels may be found in each setting. Real people grow older and more dependent in settings in which they were originally relatively independent. Not only do many of them not want to move but there are not the places at the right time, in the right area and at the right price for them to move into.

Geriatric hospital wards and private nursing homes have only small proportions in the lowest dependency categories while about half their patients are in the highest dependency categories.[83] Local authority homes have higher proportions of people in the high-dependency categories and two out of five people in the private rest home sector are in the higher-dependency categories. Rather than moving as they become more dependent people become more dependent in the setting to which they originally moved when they gave up their family homes. In response to this pattern the boundaries between the various types of institutional care are starting to be eroded. The old model is being replaced by one in which all settings are seen primarily as providing a *home* with services being added in for specific individuals as and when necessary. The services and care elements no longer attach to the type of institution but are progressively introduced for those clients or patients who actually require them.

This has major implications for the physical design and layout of nursing homes, residential homes and even sheltered housing. It also helps to promote the supportive model of care. The view that the residential elements of provision are essentially the same whether in a geriatric ward, nursing home, residential home or local authority home has far-reaching implications for the deployment of nursing staff. Most care in all settings is given by unqualified staff whether they be called *care staff* or *nursing auxiliaries*. That there are people in residential and local authority homes who need *nursing* and those in private nursing homes who may not can be seen as an argument for more appropriate placement and relocation. It can, alternatively, be seen as an argument for making more sensible use of the qualified nursing skills which are available outside the hospital setting. It is largely this element which makes private nursing homes more expensive than residential homes. Many owners of small nursing homes are themselves nurses[84] and provide a large element of the 24-hour, first-level nurse cover that is required by the registering authorities. At the same time there are many nurses who run residential homes but who are not allowed to give *nursing* care under the present legislation unless they opt for dual registration. Community nurses have to come in to give injections to residents despite the presence of a Registered General Nurse on site.

Some nursing homes are already finding it difficult to recruit first-level nurses in sufficient numbers to provide 24-hour cover and many owner-nurses are putting in long hours on call. Even if the demand for nursing home places were to spiral in the wake of any introduction of needs assessment for supplementary benefit claimants in residential care[85] it is difficult to see how a further proliferation of homes can be staffed to current standards unless more qualified nursing posts are axed from the NHS.

Of concern to nurses

Dependency of all kinds, interpersonal, organizational and structural, must be of interest to nurses. In the first place, nurses work in settings in which people are often temporarily or permanently highly dependent. The way in which they interact with patients or manage wards may encourage that dependency or alternatively may assist patients to regain their independence to a greater or lesser degree. There is no neutral stance. Without a proper analysis and awareness of what is going on in a ward setting individual nurses may be working in opposing directions. Patients may then be locked into situations where independence is promoted by some staff and undermined by others, where dependency is overtly resisted but covertly reinforced.

The notion of dependency is inextricably related to infancy and childhood; a state of being totally reliant on an adult for everything. The infant gradually emerges from that state of dependency and landmarks like walking, talking, feeding, continence, dressing and coping with minor accidents are rewarded by parents. This state of total dependence on others has very close parallels in the care of the unconscious patient with a similar kind of reward pattern encouraging initial signs of regaining capacities for self-care. Dependency is the expression of a relationship between people, one of whom needs or wants the care and the other who gives the care and gets satisfaction from meeting the needs of others. In the child–parent relationship the maturation process counterbalances the need of the parent to keep the child dependent and the child finally emerges more or less independent, self-motivating and self-directing. With the elderly, the needs of the carer and the elderly person converge in such a way that the carer may promote increasing dependence on the part of the elderly person unless there is a very strong commitment to the idea of maintaining or enhancing self-care abilities. The nursing model explicitly adopted in wards for the elderly is of crucial concern. Often there is no explicit model and the implicit model turns out to be one which creates dependency.

This very dependency of elderly people is one of the things that attracts some staff into working in geriatric wards. The *second childhood* aspects of senility are seen as attractive or perhaps it is only by responding to elderly people as large, overgrown babies that it is possible for some people to cope with the intimacies of bodily care which are the daily round and common task. Can the willingness of such people to work with the elderly be harnessed without, at the same time, promoting dependency?

The care of the elderly remains a low-status area both for medicine and nursing. The introduction of the English National Board 941 course and the inclusion of a special module in basic training has helped, as will the Diploma in Geriatric Medicine for doctors. Patients in geriatric wards do not always get the technical and support services available to patients in other wards. They do not get as much nursing time as patients of equivalent dependency in other wards and a higher proportion of the care that they do get is given by unqualified staff.

Dependency is associated with rationing. The systematic assessment of needs is often avoided because it is clear that such needs when *discovered* cannot always be met. The redeployment of existing staff to meet unanticipated fluctuations in workload merely equalizes the load. It does not even guarantee that those in the higher dependency groups are getting sufficient nursing time. The use of dependency assessment in relation to staffing levels does, however, allow nurse managers and ward sisters to demonstrate in objective, consistent and comparable terms where shortfalls are occurring. They are then in a position to make rational bids for appropriate staffing levels and resources.

Use of dependency classification helps to promote the regular assessment of patient progress. This does not conflict with the view that a patient is unique, with a unique range of problems. It simply ensures that while nurses are properly concerned with each patient on his or her own terms, the management of nursing care for a ward population can also be monitored and evaluated.

Nurses participate in decisions about the discharge of patients and, in the case of the elderly, this must always involve consideration of whether a particular individual will be able to manage at home or whether some alternative placement should be sought. A dependency assessment, whether formal or informal, is one of the major contributions to such decisions. The use of a standard classification makes it easier for a ward sister to contribute effectively to the discussion.

Particular homes differ in the extent to which they are able or willing to accept more highly dependent patients and a method of assessment which is understood and accepted by doctors, nurses, social workers, matrons of nursing homes and managers of residential homes is of vital importance.

Nurses are involved in the registration and inspection of nursing homes which in the main cater for elderly people. The policy of the health authority on the design and layout of homes, on staffing and on the type of care regime to be adopted will itself be instrumental in creating or controlling dependency. Authorities differ in their interpretation of the NAHA guidelines, some promoting clinical settings with protective models of care, others espousing supportive models with a strong emphasis on privacy, choice and the *domestic* character of the environment. Nurses can influence these policies.

The legislation on dual registration means that the designated senior nurse must adopt some standard way of differentiating between people who need *nursing* care and those who need only *residential* care. A dependency assessment measure provides one way of doing this. At least two-thirds of the patients in private nursing homes are in the higher dependency groups and clearly require nursing care. It would seem reasonable to expect that many of the 40 per cent of residents in these dependency groups are also in need of nursing care.

Joint inspection and co-operation between local authority and nursing staff is essential if dual registration is not to become a bureaucratic nightmare instead of a positive development in the care of the elderly. Joint acceptance of the needs assessment of residents and patients must surely be one of the objectives of this working together. The legal requirement that nursing homes must also seek dual registration if four or more patients are of the type more suited to residential settings, *that is are less dependent*, must go some way towards preventing the substitution effect envisaged by Challis even if needs assessment for nursing homes is not introduced at the same time as it is for prospective residential clients. This is a highly political issue and one in which nurses, as representatives of the health authorities, should not be manipulated into taking up confrontational positions in relation to those registering, inspecting and assessing clients on behalf of the local authorities. It is to be hoped that the spread of dual registered homes will make it easier to provide the necessary care in the place where the elderly person is and that, sooner rather than later, registration of homes which are so similar and which do cater for people of all dependencies will be brought under one body.

Nurses may themselves own, run or work in nursing homes and residential homes, the rationale for the existence of which lies in the dependency of the patients or residents. Some argue that because patients or residents are *paying* to be cared for they should not be expected to do things for themselves. This is also a view that may be forcefully expressed by patients and relatives. For patients in hospital the regaining of independence is the key to discharge. In nursing homes and residential homes this objective may be less immediate or unattainable. The negative corollaries of allowing patients to become more dependent have to be clearly spelled out to staff and patients alike. Some home owners are very keen to promote independence and see it as part of their role to rehabilitate patients sufficiently for them to move to other forms of care. Others are less committed.

Let us hope that more of us who are involved with the elderly may share with the imaginary and imaginative Jane Somers her new-found understanding.

The Welfare are trying to 'rehabilitate' Annie. I would have reacted, only a few weeks ago, to the invitation to this campaign, with derision, even with cries of But it is cruelty! Since then, I've seen Eliza's life, and understand why these experts with the old will fight the lethargy of age even in a man or women of ninety or more.[86]

References

1. Bassey, J., 'The case for exercise in later life'. Paper read at day conference on *New Initiatives in Health Care*, Stafford, 3 December 1986.
2. The Foundation for Age Research and the Health Education Council, *The Agile 80's*. Papers read at a day conference in London on 12 November 1986.
3. Blaikie, A. and Macnicol, J., 'Towards an anatomy of ageism: society, social policy and the elderly between the wars'. In Phillipson, C., Bernard, M. and Strang, P. (eds), *Dependency and Interdependency in Old Age*. Croom Helm, London, 1986.
4. Townsend, P., 'The structured dependency of the elderly: a creation of social policy in the twentieth century', *Ageing and Society*, 1981, **1**, Part 1, pp. 5–28.
5. See reference 4, p. 9.
6. Morris, P., *Put Away*. Routledge & Kegan Paul, London, 1969.
7. Goffman, E., *Asylums*. Anchor Books (Doubleday & Co.), London, 1961.
8. Phillipson, C., Bernard, M., and Strang, P. (eds), *Dependency and Interdependency in Old Age*. Croom Helm, London, 1986.
9. Fisk, M. J., *Independence and the Elderly*. Croom Helm, London, 1986.

10. *All our tomorrows: Growing old in Britain.* Report of the British Medical Association's Board of Science and Education, 1986.
11. Lester, P. and Baltes, M., 'Functional interdependence of the social environment and behaviour of the active aged', *Journal of Gerontological Nursing*, 1978, **4**, No. 2, 22–27.
12. Miller, A., 'Does dependency count?' *Senior Nurse*, 1984, **1**, No. 29, 10–12.
13. Evers, H., 'Tender loving care?—patients and nurses in geriatric wards'. In Copp, L. A., *Care of the Ageing*. Churchill Livingstone, Edinburgh, 1981.
14. Godlove, C. and Dunn, G., with Wright, H., 'Caring for old people in New York and London: The nurses' aide interviews', *Journal of the Royal Society of Medicine*, 1980, **73**, 713–724.
15. Auden, W. S., *The English Auden.* Faber & Faber, London, 1977, p. 51.
16. Williamson, C., 'What's in a name?', *Nursing Times*, 1984, 28 November, 30–32.
17. Department of Health and Social Security, *Growing Older.* HMSO, London, 1981.
18. *Home life: a code of practice for residential care*, Centre for Policy on Ageing, London, 1984.
19. See reference 13.
20. Mabon, G., 'Muddy Waters', *Care Concern*, 1987 (January/February), 12–13.
21. Department of Health and Social Security, *Nurse Manpower Project for NHS Management Inquiry.* HMSO, London, 1984.
22. Ball, J., 'A quality environment', *Senior Nurse*, 1987, **6**, No. 1, 23–24.
23. MacGuire, J. M. and Newberry, S. R., 'A measure of need', *Senior Nurse*, 1984, **1**, No. 17, 14–18.
24. MacGuire, J. M., 'Where do we go from here?', *Senior Nurse*, 1986, **5**, No. 5/6, 12–15.
25. Harris, A., *Handicapped and Impaired in Great Britain.* Social Survey Division of the Office of Population Censuses and Surveys, HMSO, London, 1971.
26. Audit Commission, *Making a Reality of Community Care.* HMSO, London, 1986.
27. Bansal, D. V., 'Care and cure of the nonagenarians'. Paper read at the Annual Conference of the British Society of Gerontology at the University of Keele, 27–29 September 1985.
28. Department of Health and Social Security, *Inequalities in Health*, Report of a Research Working Group, HMSO, London, 1980.
29. See reference 4.
30. See reference 26, p. 19.
31. Department of Health and Social Security, *A Handbook of Policies and Priorities for Health and Personal Services in England.* HMSO, London, 1981.
32. Bartlett, H. and Challis, L., 'Surveying the boom in private nursing homes', *Health and Social Services Journal*, 1985, 13 June, p. 738.
33. Challis, L., Day, P. and Klein, R., 'Residential care on demand', *New Society*, 1984, 5 April, p. 32.
34. See reference 26.

35. *Observer*, 1987, 1 February.
36. National Association of Health Authorities in England and Wales, *Registration and Inspection of Nursing Homes*, Annex B, 1985.
37. See reference 20.
38. See reference 36, para 18.3, p. 35.
39. See reference 8.
40. Bergman, R. and Golander, H., 'Evaluation of care for the aged: a multipurpose guide', *Journal of Advanced Nursing*, 1982, **7**, 203–210.
41. Sainsbury, S., *Measuring Disability*. Occasional Papers on Social Administration, No. 54, Bell and Sons, London, 1973.
42. Orem, D., *Nursing: Concepts of Practice*. McGraw Hill, New York, 1971.
43. Barr, A., *Measurement of Nursing Care*. Oxford Regional Hospital Board, Oxford, 1967.
44. Mulligan, B., *Measurement of Patient–Nurse Dependency and Work Load Index*. King's Fund Centre, London, 1973.
45. Barr, A., 'A review of the various methods of measuring the dependency of patients on nursing staff', *International Journal of Nursing Studies*, 1973, **10**, No. 3.
46. Norwich, H. S., 'A study of nursing care in geriatric hospitals', *Nursing Times*, 1980, 14 February, 292–295.
47. Rhys-Hearn, C. and Howard, J., 'The relationship of nursing needs, resources and standards in geriatric wards', *Management Services and the Nurse*. Paper read at conference, Harrogate, 1979, 27 & 28 September.
48. Wade, B. E. and Snaith, P., 'The assessment of patients' needs for nursing care in geriatric wards', *International Journal of Nursing Studies*, 1981, **18**, No. 4, pp. 261–271.
49. Cheltenham and District Health Authority, *A Step-by-Step Guide to Undertake a Nursing Dependency Study in a Hospital for Elderly Patients*, Cheltenham, 1983 revised 1984.
50. Mid-Staffordshire Health Authority, *Stafford KTC Formula: The Mid-Staffordshire Dependency System*, Stafford, 1984.
51. Ball, J. A., Goldstone, L. A. and Collier, M. M., *Criteria for Care, The Manual of the North West Nurse Staffing Levels Project*. Newcastle upon Tyne Polytechnic Products Ltd, Newcastle upon Tyne, 1984.
52. Northern Regional Health Authority, *Report on Evaluation of Aberdeen Formula for Calculating Nurse Establishments in Hospital Wards*, Northern Regional Hospital Board, 1978.
53. Trent Regional Health Authority, *Leicestershire Health Authority: An Investigation into the nurse staffing requirements at the Leicester Royal Infirmary*, Report No. 807/6, 1982.
54. Scottish Home and Health Department, *Nursing workload per patient as a basis for staffing*. Scottish Health Service Studies, No. 9, Edinburgh, 1969.
55. Edgecumbe, R. H., 'The C.A.S.H. approach to hospital management engineering', *Hospitals*, 1965, **39**, No. 6, pp. 70–74.
56. Senior, O., *Dependency and Establishments*. Royal College of Nursing, London, 1979.
57. Wilson-Barnett, J., *Review of Patient Nurse Dependency Studies*, DHSS Nurse Research Liaison Group, London, 1978.
58. See reference 21.

59. Goldstone, L. A., Ball, J. A. and Collier, M. M., *Monitor*. Newcastle upon Tyne Polytechnic Products Ltd, Newcastle upon Tyne, 1983.
60. Fillerbaum, G., *The Well Being of the Elderly: Approaches to Multidimensional Assessment*. World Health Organisation, Geneva, 1984.
61. Wade, B., Sawyer, L. and Bell, J., *Dependency with Dignity: Different Care Provision for the Elderly*. Bedford Square Press/NCVO, London, 1983.
62. Macdonald, A. J. D., Mann, A. H., Jenkins, R., Richard, L., Godlove, C. and Rodwell, G., 'An attempt to determine the impact of four types of care upon the elderly in London by the study of matched groups', *Psychological Medicine*, 1982, **12**, No. 1, pp. 193–200.
63. Atkinson, D. A., Bond, J. and Gregson, B. A., 'The dependency characteristics of older people in long-term institutional care'. In reference 8.
64. Booth, T., 'Institutional regimes and resident outcomes in homes for the elderly'. In reference 8.
65. Coles, O., 'Dependency trends in homes for the elderly: what do they show?'. Paper read at conference, University of Keele, 1986, 27–29 September.
66. See reference 21.
67. *Mix and Match: A Review of Nursing Skill Mix*. Report of a working group presented to the Chief Nursing Officer, Department of Health and Social Security, 1986.
68. United Kingdom Central Council, *Code of Professional Conduct* 2nd edition, 1984.
69. Gray, A., 'A mixed review', *Senior Nurse*, 1987, **6**, No. 2, pp. 7–8.
70. *Report of the NHS Management Inquiry*, Chairman Roy Griffiths. DA(83)38, Department of Health and Social Security, London, 1983.
71. Moores, B. and Barr, A., 'Nurse patient dependency revisited (somewhat apologetically)', *Journal of Advanced Nursing*, 1982, **7**, No. 3, pp. 269–271.
72. See reference 67.
73. See reference 61.
74. Roper, N. and Logan, W., 'The Roper/Logan/Tierney Model', *Senior Nurse*, 1985, **3**, No. 2, pp. 20–26.
75. See reference 42.
76. Wright, S., 'Quality matters', *Senior Nurse*, 1984, **1**, No. 19, pp. 16–19.
77. See reference 48, p. 202.
78. See reference 13.
79. Salvage, A. V., *Attitudes of the over 75s to Health and Social Services*. Research Team for the care of the Elderly, University of Wales College of Medicine, 1986.
80. See reference 26.
81. Challis, L., 'Robbing Peter to pay Paul—handsomely', *Social Services Insight*, 1986, 16–23 August, pp. 12–14.
82. Challis, L. and Bartlett, H., 'The paying patients: customer or commodity'. In reference 8.
83. See reference 48, p. 65.
84. Bartlett, H. and Challis, L., *Private Nursing Homes for the Elderly*. Working Paper 3, Centre for the Analysis of Social Policy, University of Bath (n.d.).

85. See reference 81.
86. Lessing, Doris, *The Diaries of Jane Somers*. Penguin Books, Harmonds-
    worth, 1985, p. 155.

Political Issues in Nursing: Past, Present and Future, Volume 3
Edited by R. White
© 1988 John Wiley & Sons Ltd

CHAPTER 6

Challenging role boundaries: conceptual frameworks for understanding the conflict arising from the implementation of the nursing process in practice

DIRK M. KEYZER, RGN, DANS, MSc, PhD
Projects Co-ordination Officer, Welsh National Board for Nursing, Midwifery and Health Visiting, Pearl Assurance House, Greyfriars Road, Cardiff, Wales

Introduction

The current move towards the introduction of a nursing model in practice and education can be traced back to an education policy document distributed to schools of nursing by the then General Nursing Council for England and Wales (GNC).[1] Following the setting up of the United Kingdom Central Council for Nursing, Midwifery and Health Visiting (UKCC), and the National Boards, under the terms of the Nurses, Midwives and Health Visitors Act 1979, this policy was supported by these new statutory bodies.[2,3]

The gap between the existing role of the nurse and that advocated in the nursing model for care was acknowledged by the UKCC.[2] Ashworth, Castledine and McFarlane[4] and Webb[5] argued that the adoption of a nursing model in practice demanded a reorientation in the nurse's knowledge, skills and attitudes and a shift in the distribution of power and control in favour of the clinical nurse.

The problems involved in introducing the nursing process in practice were underlined by Clark[6] when she identified the nurse's rejection of the new approach to care. This rejection is founded in the ethos of nursing organizations which denies the intellectual aspects of the 'nursing' model. Similarly, Holmes[7] cited Ashworth to argue that eight years after the distribution of the GNC policy document,[1] there were still areas of the United Kingdom where the nursing process had hardly been heard of, and others where the concept was understood, but not its complexity.

In those areas where the nursing process has been applied to practice, many nurses have adopted the concept of their role as presented by Henderson[8] and others.[9,10,11] In this concept, the nurse is perceived to function as an autonomous practitioner prescribing, implementing and evaluating the patient's needs for nursing care. Central to this role is the belief in the patient's right to be an active participant in the health-care programme.

It is this 'practitioner' role for the nurse and the active 'participant' role for the patient which challenges the power structures of the traditional nursing organizations. The development of the traditional nursing role reflects the role and status of women throughout the nineteenth and twentieth centuries. Maggs[12] drew on the work of Summers[13] and Storr[14] to identify the close links between nursing and women's work in general and the way in which nursing has offered social and occupational mobility to working-class women, that would otherwise not have been open to them. Davies[15,16] argued that the division of labour between the professional nurse and the woman in her own home was based on social factors, rather than technical expertise. Further, nurses have developed an occupational strategy which refers decision-making upwards and creates a dependency on doctors in times of conflict.[15,17] This is supported by Bygraves[18] who stated that nurses were still avoiding political issues affecting patient care and their role.

Nursing carries all the hallmarks of a female occupation: limited access to education, high turnover of staff in the clinical area, subservience to the predominantly male occupation of medicine, a career structure limited to management.[19]

Dingwall and McIntosh[20] cited Whittaker and Olesen to show how the Nightingale myth can be used to lower the self-esteem of the student, which, in turn, creates a non-assertive practitioner. Even Nightingale herself, as the role model for the myth, never stepped over the boundaries of what was expected of a Victorian lady.[21] Nursing would therefore appear to be founded in a gender division of labour and a dualist labour market.

The occasion when nurses enhanced their organizational position was following the implementation of the Salmon Report.[22] The traditional Nightingale strategies had always placed the emphasis on the managerial role of the nurse.[21,23] By creating an expanded hierarchy and the career structure in management, the Salmon Report reinforced nursing politics by giving nurses a greater say in the decision-making of the organization. Could it be that the hidden political strategy behind the implementation of the nursing process and a practitioner-orientated division of labour is to extend the nurse's say in decision-making in the clinical area?

The implementation of the 'practitioner' role desired by the profession,[1,3,24] while appealing to the political ambitions of nurse leaders challenges the existing distribution of power and control and the strategies which maintain role boundaries within the nursing organization. It is this challenge to the traditional power structures which is a possible source of conflict for the clinical nurse attempting to implement the national, organizational and professional policies for the 'practitioner' role of the nurse.

In this chapter the focus will be on the following themes: (1) the distribution of power and control in nursing organizations; (2) its effect on the model for nursing practice; and (3) its effect on the division of labour in the nurse–patient relationship. The conceptual frameworks of 'codes and control' developed by the writer from that constructed by Bernstein[25] for general education and adapted by Beattie and Durguerian[26] for health-care organizations, are presented to explain the conflict between the traditional role of the nurse and that inherent in the nursing model for care. It will be argued that the distribution of power and control in society is reflected in the model for practice adopted by the organization. The introduction of a new framework for practice which challenges this social and organizational power structure will be resisted by the powerholders whose control over practice it seeks to alter.[11]

Implementing the nursing process in one health authority: the problems of conflict in the implementation of change in nursing practice

In the study for which the 'codes and control' frameworks were developed, the writer, in the role of an observer who participates, negotiated clinically based learning contracts with the nurses working in one community hospital, one long-stay geriatric unit, one psychiatric rehabilitation unit and one psycho-geriatric assessment unit. The units were located in four hospitals of one health authority. Thus general psychiatric and community nurses are represented in this study of the management of knowledge and change in nursing practice.[11]

A variety of data-collecting techniques was used to provide an illuminative evaluation of the implementation of the nursing process in practice and education. The formal approach to education was represented by the Diploma in Nursing (London University, Old and New Regulations) and the Joint Board of Clinical Nursing Studies Course 941. The non-formal imputs were the clinically based learning contracts.

The data are presented as comparative case-studies which record the organizational policies adopted by the health authority and the effect these policies had on the nurse's attempts to promote the new mode of practice in the clinical area. One of the themes to emerge from the recorded data is that of role conflict.

In line with the guidelines distributed by the GNC[1] the Health Authority's Nursing Policy Group adopted the nursing process as the desired mode of practice on 16 February 1981. To support this change in practice the then Area Nursing Officer set up the Nursing Process Development Group. From the records held by the Nursing Policy Group and the Nursing Process Development Group certain anomalies appeared in the implementation of the nursing process.[11]

These problems arose in part from the organizational status of the Nursing Process Development Group. This group's organizational power was vested in the 'personal', rather than 'positional' power of the Area Nursing Officer. It had no authority to allocate or reallocate the resources required to implement the organizational policy on the nursing process. The data recorded in the study identify that previous attempts to implement change in the role of the nurse had failed from a lack of support from nursing and medical staff.[11a] Thus, it appeared that the top level of nurse managers were unable to support the innovations they encouraged. The status of the Nursing Process Development Group was challenged by nurse managers in the psychiatric hospital. This challenge stemmed from a debate on the adverse effect the staff:patient ratio had on the charge nurse's attendance at meetings organized by the Nursing Process Development Group and the day-release study days of the Diploma in Nursing (London University, Old and New Regulations).

The data recorded also identified how the constant changes in the membership of the group, resulting from the frequent turnover of staff in the clinical areas, affected the progress made by the individual units and the group as a whole.[11b]

One year after the initial policy decision had been taken by the Nursing Policy Group to implement the nursing process in practice, the records kept by the Nursing Process Development Group indicated that the requisite resources needed to achieve this goal were still not available. The impression given by these records is that of a group of highly motivated nurses going from one organizational group to another, begging for the resources to implement national, organizational and professional policies for change in the clinical role. An attempt to raise the needed resources through the submission of a research proposal to the Area Research Committee received the following reply: 'the request for funding from the Area Research Committee had been refused on the postal vote, the voting being 8–2 against . . . the Chairman has expressed his regret.'[11c]

Throughout the study the nurses identified the conflict arising from the lack of financial and educational resources. In an attempt to reject the medical model in practice, the lack of 'nursing' knowledge forced the practitioners back into the traditional model. In this way the medical profession's control over the development of the role of the nurse was ensured. The power of the medical profession's control over the development of the nursing role is subtle. By adopting the medical model in practice and education, the clinical nurse becomes dependent on medical knowledge to explain patient behaviour. The use of the medical perspective ensures that further medical knowledge is needed to develop the service offered to the patient.

The medical profession's control over the development of the clinical role of the nurse is further enhanced through the doctor's legal responsibility for the patient. Thus, this control over the nurse can be exerted through the physician's relationship with the patient. In the study only the consultant psychiatrist used this power to control the development of the implementation of the nursing process in an overt manner. The control exerted by the medical profession in the other units in this study was more covert; it was never the less just as effective.[11]

The organizational attitudes towards the elderly and those who cared for them were represented in the case-studies. The data suggested that the staff in the geriatric units perceived their work as physically hard and detrimental to their careers. They had not applied for these posts of their own free will. As one newly qualified staff nurse stated: 'I am not really worried by my allocation to a geriatric ward for my first post.

My tutor said that I was a good student and that I should not have to wait too long for a real ward'.[11d]

In keeping the innovation of the nursing process to its least prestigious area, was the organization trying to protect its more valued, medically dominated, high-technology areas from the risks inherent in change? If it was, then there was a covert strategy which valued the traditional role over that inherent in the nursing process and adopted by the Area Nursing Policy Group. This would appear to be a real source of conflict for any nurse attempting to implement the 'practitioner' role instead of the traditional 'organizational' role.

Evidence to support this hypothesis that the organization preferred the traditional role over that contained in the nursing process was identified in the patient handouts distributed by the community hospital. This community hospital had openly adopted the nursing process as the basis for practice and had instituted a 'primary' nursing role for the staff nurse and a 'practitioner' role for the nursing officer. The official description of the nursing role did not support this model of care. The data presented in this patient handout stated that the doctor was the person who 'cared' for the patient and controlled the patient's access to other health-care workers; these other health-care workers, for example physiotherapists, occupational therapists and speech therapists, played important professional roles in planning patient care. Nurses however, were perceived to be: 'keeping in touch with other professional groups to make sure that the patients get help they need in the hospital and at home'.[11e] This is hardly the 'practitioner' role described in the literature of the nursing process;[8] rather, it smacks of the traditional role of the nurse taking on aspects of care other health workers leave out under the rationale of providing 'total patient care'.[15,17]

In its management of the change towards the preferred 'practitioner' role the organization would appear to have isolated the change to its least desirable clinical areas, to have starved these clinical areas of the resources needed to implement the change and to have denied the nurse access to the educational programmes required to develop the 'practitioner' role. Why did the organization adopt the nursing process as policy and then appear to do everything to prevent its implementation? To understand this apparent paradox a framework which addresses itself to the organizational structures which maintain role boundaries and the strategies which support the status quo between the roles of the doctor, the nurse and the patient, is needed.

Theoretical frameworks for understanding conflict in practice and education: a 'code and control' model

Bernstein's[25] theoretical formulation is an attempt to understand the inter-relationship between symbolic orders, forms of social organization and the shaping of experience in terms of codes. Using this framework the changes in the organization, transmission and evaluation of educational knowledge may be viewed as the reflection of the social distribution of power and the principles of social control.

Educational knowledge codes are defined as the underlying principles which shape curriculum, pedagogy and evaluation. The form these codes take depends on social principles which regulate classification and framing of the knowledge made public in educational institutions.

The concept of classification refers not to what is classified, but to the relationship between contents. Where classification is strong (C+), the contents are well insulated from each other by strong boundaries. When classification is weak (C−), the boundaries between contents are open and blurred. Classification therefore refers to the degree of boundary maintenance between contents.[25]

The concept of frame is used to determine the structure of the message system, pedagogy. Frame refers to the form of the context in which knowledge is transmitted and received. Frame therefore is concerned with the relationship of the teacher and the student. Frame is defined as the strength of the boundary between what may be transmitted and what may not. Where framing is strong (F+) the boundary is sharp, where framing is weak (F−), a blurred and open boundary exists between what may and may not be transmitted.[25]

Beattie and Durguerian[26] applied Bernstein's framework of 'codes and control' to the education and practice of 'Family Planning' nurses. In doing so they illustrated the conflict between the 'curriculum' model of the nursing role set out in the theoretical content of the course and the 'discipline' model experienced in the 'real' world of the clinic. The writers also identified the colonization of a self-help group by professionals and the subsequent loss of control over the service by the social group for whom the service was initially intended and who were responsible for the organization and delivery of the service.

Thus, the effectiveness of any service organization depends on the wider social, professional and organizational factors which shape that service. An understanding of this aspect of health care is essential for the planning of the service provided in terms of available resources, technology and trained staff.[26] Beattie and Durguerian draw our attention to the use of 'organisational' and 'occupational' models in the past to account for the social tensions and conflicts within organizations, to understand the creation of role boundaries and the division of labour within the organization and between different occupational groups. Webb[5] also utilized Bernstein's framework and argued that the 'codes and control' framework identified the need to redistribute the power of decision-making between the manager and the clinical nurse in any attempt to implement the nursing process. Whereas Beattie and Durguerian[26] utilized a two-dimensional plane, Webb drew only a continuum between 'personal' and 'positional' power in the traditional nursing organization.[5]

The changing model for nursing practice

In the pre-Nightingale model (Figure 1) the boundary between what is and what is not nursing is open and blurred (C−).[21] The role of the nurse in the home and the hospital was fixed in the role and status of women. The lack of a medical framework for explaining ill health denied the doctor the social status and control he was to enjoy in the later nineteenth-century voluntary and teaching hospitals. In the hospital setting the nurse was subservient to the doctor's sapiential authority. Similarly, in the Poor Law and the Voluntary Hospitals the nurse was responsible to the nursing hierarchy for the running of the ward. In this way, bureaucratic-professional conflict was integral to the hospital nurse's role. The patient played no active role in the plan of care and was expected to be a passive recipient of care. It was only in the homes of the wealthy that the patient, as master of the household, controlled the doctor through direct payment for services received. Nursing care in this setting was provided by trusted servants and female relatives.[21,23] The model for practice is, therefore, defined as one of weak classification (C−) and strong framing (F+) (Figure 1).

With the introduction of the Nightingale school and the rise of the medical profession as an institution of social control through its increased knowledge base, the distribution of power and control between the doctor and the patient changed. With an established power base in the teaching hospital and a right to define health and illness, the doctor established control over the patient regardless of the health-care setting.[21,23]

Medical care was then controlled by the middle-class doctor and responsibility for running the hospital placed in the hands of his female counterpart, the matron. The giving of direct patient care was, however,

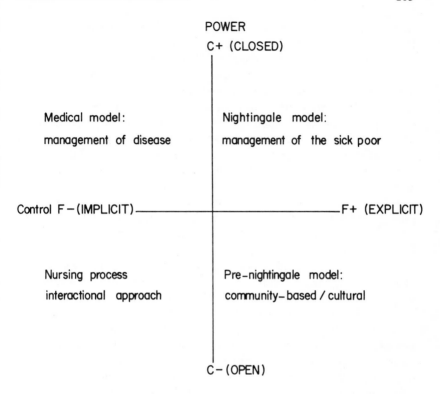

Figure 1. Models for nursing practice (after Bernstein, 1975; Beattie and Durguerian, 1980)

still in the hands of the 'domestic' classes.[14,21,23] In political terms the introduction of the Nightingale school had provided the nurse with a tenure of office denied to her pre-Nightingale counterpart. The matron, surrounded by her assistants, had access to the decision-makers in the form of the doctor and the administrator.[23]

The medical profession enhanced its control over the role of the nurse at the bedside through the adoption of the medical model in education. The introduction of the Nightingale school had, therefore, enhanced the nurse's social and organizational status through the provision of an apprenticeship-type training and a tenure of office. Within the provision of care the patient's role of passive recipient was consolidated through the organizational and emerging social roles of the doctor and the nurse in the management of the sick poor.[21,23] The model for practice now becomes one of strong classification (C+), strong framing (F+) (Figure 1). The boundaries between the roles of the doctor, the nurse and the patient are clearly insulated by the rising social power of the doctor and the education needed to be recognized as a nurse. Within the nursing hierarchy power remained as before, that is positional rather than personal (Figure 1).

As the early twentieth century progressed nursing politics demanded that the boundaries between what was considered to be the role of the professional nurse and mere mothering be tightened up.[21] This was achieved through the Nurse' Act 1919. This consolidation of the nurse's organizational and social power was, however, a double-edged sword. White[28] argued that the introduction of the GNC, following the Nurse's Act 1919, gave central government the power needed to limit the growing aspirations of the nursing profession. What the Act did was to seal the role boundaries between the roles of the nurse and the woman in her own home.

Following the Second World War and an explosion of knowledge and technology, which reinforced medicine's claims as an institution of social control, the role of the nurse changed. The value given to the nurse's role began to veer towards those areas of clinical practice that brought the nurse into close contact with doctors and medical technology. The nurse, therefore, became more reliant on the doctor's knowledge base to guide her practice and thereby enhanced his control over her job content. This sudden change in nursing practice outstripped the manager's control over the nurse. Clinical nurses were now carrying out tasks their managers had never practised. A compromise had to be reached.

Within the organization, the clinical nurse achieved some control over her role through the taking on of tasks the doctor no longer wished to carry out. His permission to take on the tasks was required, as was his knowledge base. Medicine thereby increased its control over the development of the role of the nurse. Within the hierarchy of nursing, the implementation of the Salmon Report[22] gave the nurse manager the political power to extend her control over the organizational decision-making on a more equal basis *vis-à-vis* the doctor and the administrator. By taking on the reflected glory of the doctor in the medically dominated, high-technology area of patient care and the career structure in management, nursing could begin to reject those aspects of care it considered to be 'non-nursing' tasks. The era of the nurse technician and manager had arrived. In the medical model, based on the management of disease (Figure 1), the model for nursing practice becomes one of strong classification (C+), weak framing (F−). The freedom given to the nurse in this model is more apparent than real. The degree of freedom given to the nurse is tightly controlled by the doctor, the manager and, through the GNC, the government.

Within the nursing organization there would be some nurses who exercised greater control over their job content than others. This degree of freedom depended on the perception of the role held by the power-holders. Thus a model for practice reflecting strong classification (C+), strong framing (F+) could be found coexisting with one based on strong classification (C+), weak framing (F−) (Figure 1).

Throughout its historical development as an occupation, nursing has drawn its social and organizational power from its close proximity to medicine. Its main role has been one of a transmitter of medicine's power in the provision of medically dominated care systems. In the mid-1970s nursing suddenly adopted a 'nursing' framework for practice which originated as a teaching tool in the United States of America.[29] This 'nursing' model of care originated in a social system where medicine and nursing were firmly rooted in the market place. The patient's right to be involved in all aspects of the therapeutic plan stems from his position in the cash nexus. A process of nursing, derived from the cultural and social setting of health care in America, may not be the same thing as the nursing process originating in the United Kingdom.[29]

These American frameworks, for example Henderson[8] and Roy,[30] emphasize the autonomous role of the nurse practitioner and the active participation of the client and suggest a model for practice based on weak classification (C−), weak framing (F−). On further analysis, these frameworks imbue the nurse with greater power than the patient. It is the nurse who assesses, plans, intervenes and evaluates, rather than the patient. Thus, while the frameworks outwardly appear to suggest a patient-centred approach which challenges the traditional power and control of the nurse and doctor (Figure 1), in reality they could be used to reinforce existing organizational power structures. The model for practice suggested by Henderson[8] and Roy[30] could, therefore, be seen to lie along a continuum from strong classification (C+), strong framing (F+) to strong classification (C+), weak framing (F−) (Figure 1).

A true patient-centred model for nursing practice, which imbues the client with the power over decision-making, would be a direct challenge to the tightly controlled boundaries (C+) between the roles of the doctor, the nurse and the woman in her own home (Figures 1 and 2). It is unlikely that such a model for practice would be welcomed by those whose power it seeks to remove.

The dichotomy between theory and practice

The application of the 'codes and control' framework to the data collected in the study of the implementation of the nursing process clarifies the paradox recorded in the case-studies.[11] The adoption of the nursing process with its emphasis on the clinical 'practitioner' role of the nurse and the patient as the central focus of the nursing actions reinforces the traditional concept of 'total patient care'. This concept, as discussed by Bendall,[31] had never been practised in the reality of the ward setting. Its main function was one of 'reifying' the existence of the professional nurse and, as such, was satisfying to the nurse in maintaining her social and organizational status.[31]

If the organization could contain the implementation of the nursing process to a continuation of the concept of 'total patient care', then not only would it serve the purpose of nursing politics, it would not challenge the existing distribution of power and control in the relationships held by the nurses *vis-à-vis* the patient, the manager and the doctor. Was this the hidden strategy recorded in the case-studies? The answer to this question will be determined by future nurse historians researching this period of change. In the meantime, the data recorded in the study provide an account of the attempts made by a group of nurses to implement the nursing process in their clinical areas and the management of that change by the organization. This data suggested that the current move towards the redistribution of power and control in the provision of nursing care is in danger of becoming an extension of the traditional Nightingale strategies aimed at enhancing the status of the nurse.

Further evidence to support this hypothesis is supplied by Hollingworth.[32] In a study of an education programme aimed at preparing nurse teachers as change agents, Hollingworth described the lack of curriculum development, based on the nursing process, in schools of nursing. This, she suggested, stemmed from the lack of leadership by those in charge of the training institutions and poor organizational hygiene. This included rigid attitudes and opposition to new ideas and practices, combined with poor communication between the schools of nursing and the clinical areas selected for nurse training. Thus, ten years after Bendall[31] described the dichotomy between theory and practice, Hollingworth pointed to the conflict experienced by students who were asked to practise the nursing process in the 'reality' of the ward without the theoretical preparation to do so. Both Keyzer[11] and Hollingworth[32] argued the need for the active involvement of all levels of nurse in the change towards the nursing model in practice and education, backed up by supportive education programmes and open channels of communication which would permit the diffusion of the innovation throughout the organization.

The United Kingdom Central Council[3] identified the confusing and overlapping roles of the different levels of nurse in the provision of nursing care. While promoting its concept of one level of practitioner to overcome these problems, no attempt was made to analyse the division of labour in health care. To understand the radical change involved in the recommendations for one level of nurse practitioner supported by 'specialist' nurses, a framework which addresses itself to

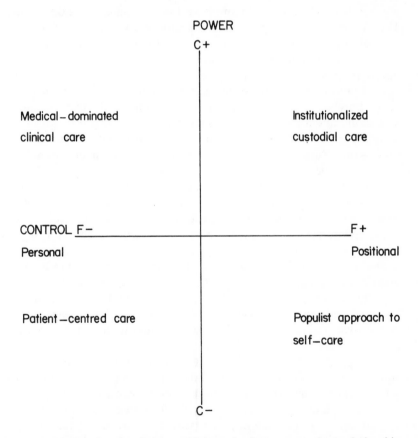

Figure 2. Models for the division of labour in the nurse–patient relationship (after Bernstein, 1975; Beattie and Durguerian, 1980)

the division of labour between the nurse, the patient and the women in her own home is required.

In the following sections Bernstein's 'codes and control' model will be applied to nurse–patient relationships in the hospital and the community setting.

Institutionalized Custodial Care

The power and control exerted by the medical profession over the role and education of the nurse and the 'positional' power of the matron in the Poor Law and Voluntary Hospitals, constrained the development of the personal power of the nurse and the patient.[5,23] This model for practice is represented in Figure 2 as 'Institutionalized/custodial' care. The division of labour between the doctor and the nurse is controlled through the doctor's expertise, his knowledge base and his social position. In the nurse–nurse relationship the boundaries between the different levels of the hierarchy are maintained through the organizational power and control over decision-making invested in each level of the bureaucracy. In this way there exists a hierarchy of tasks associated with patient care and the management of the organization.

In the nurse–patient relationship, the division of labour between professional nursing and 'mere mothering' was maintained through the statutory bodies, that is the General Nursing Councils and, later, the United Kingdom Central Council and the National Boards. White[28] argued that it was through these agencies that the government controlled the education for and the development of the role of the nurse. White provided evidence which suggested that this control was not necessarily in the interests of the nurse or the patient.

In this model for care the locus of control lay in the hands of the doctor, the nurse-manager and the nurse *vis-à-vis* the patient. As medical knowledge and technology developed, the focus of the nurse's attention became the management of the disease. This management of disease was organized on the lines of task allocation and the routinization of care.

Through the internalization of the Nightingale myth underlying the curriculum and discipline models of the role, the control over the nurse was entrenched in the obedience to the hierarchy, denial of self, referral to authority and precedence as the guidelines to solving both organizational and clinical problems. The patient in this model for care was expected to be the passive recipient of care. These needs for care were determined through the physician's diagnosis of disease and the treatments he prescribed for cure. As a manager of care the trained nurse tended to meet the needs of the organization first, at the expense of the patient's individual needs for care.[23]

The 'organizational' role developed within these hospitals maintained the boundaries between the roles of the doctor, the nurse and the patient, and between the roles of the manager, the clinical practitioner and the patient. This is represented in Figure 2 as strong classification, strong framing (C+, F+). Any attempt to introduce a model for practice which shifts the locus of control towards the clinical nurse and the patient not only upsets the balance of organizational power, it disrupts the division of labour between the powerholders and those they control. Such an attempt to disturb the role boundaries will be resisted by the powerholders and, perhaps, even individual nurses and patients who have internalized the existing power relationships.

Medically dominated health-care systems

In Figure 2 the model for care represented by strong classification, weak framing (C+, F−) is that referred to as 'Medically dominated clinical care'. This model for care is that found in the Family Practitioner Health Clinic. Here the division of labour is still maintained through the power of the professional expertise of the physician and the nurse. The patient's control over the access to the health-care services required to meet his needs for cure and care are inhibited by the doctor and his satelites: the community nurses and health visitors. Even in those instances where the patient has direct access to a nurse, for example for wound dressing, vaccination and health advice, the areas of care may have been determined by the physician's allocation of the task to the nurse and, hence, the nurse's control over the patient's direct access to treatments and aids to recovery.

In this model for care the patient can exercise some control over the therapeutic plan. He can decide whether or not to follow the instructions given, to take the drugs prescribed, or to come back for further treatments. This control over the plan of care is limited by the power of the professional expertise invested in the doctor and the nurse and their power to control his access to the formal health-care system. These professionals cannot control the influence of the patient's family, or his cultural beliefs about health, illness and the form the care should take. The patient does, therefore, exert some control over the decisions made to seek out medical advice and whether or not the prescribed actions for cure and care are carried out. He cannot bypass the physician and seek specialist expertise present in the formal health-care system.

Patient-centred care

The model for care prescribed as weak classification, weak framing (C−, F−) in Figure 2 is referred to as 'Patient-centred care'. In this model for care the focus of the nursing actions is the patient's needs for care as defined by himself, his family and his cultural group. This model is similar to that presented by King.[33]

Here, the patient and his family are perceived to be active participants in all aspects of the decision-making process and the nurse is only one of the many care-givers and resources available to the patient in his cultural and social setting. Thus, in both the community and the hospital setting, the locus of control over decision-making is invested in the patient and the 'practitioner' nurse. An early example of this type of health-care system was the original 'family planning' service set up by women's groups in this country. As stated earlier in this chapter, Beattie and Durguerian[26] described the professionalization of this group by physicians and the creation of a model represented by 'strong classification, weak framing' (C+, F−). The power over decision-making therefore transferred to the doctor. The role of the nurse as 'patient advocate' is diminished by this strong classification (C+).

The power invested in the professional health-care worker, doctor and nurse would appear to make the implementation of a true patient-centred approach to care impossible. In its place I would suggest that a possible model for care is that of weak classification, strong framing (C−, F+). In Figure 2 this model for care is defined as 'Populist self-help'. Here the tasks carried out by the nurse and the patient are ill-defined and the nurse takes her place within the socio-cultural framework for care-giving available to the patient.[27] The role of the nurse is seen to be one of applying professional expertise to the client's perceived needs for care. The nurse is, therefore, viewed as a practitioner working within the community in which the patient and she live and work. The health-care programme is one of community-based 'self-care' with the emphasis placed on health care, rather than the illness orientation of the traditional hospital-based programmes. The contractual nurse–patient relationship advocated by Orem[34] would appear to be the one most suited to this model for practice.

Current examples of self-help are Mencap and Help the Aged. These organizations function as pressure groups to help the mentally handicapped and the elderly to monitor the quality of care provided by the formal care system and to promote the wellbeing of the individual or group through support services. This model does not negate the contributions of the formal health-care system, rather it seeks to reinforce the effectiveness of that system through the active involvement of the client population. The weakness of this model lies in the concept of self-help. Tuckett[35] cited research data which suggested that those in most need are the very ones who do not have the social, educational or financial resources to engage in self-help. It therefore falls to the nurse to utilize her positional power (F+) to support the individual or group in her capacity as patient advocate.

It may also be argued that the implementation of such a model challenges the power base of the medical profession and the nurse manager. The weak classification (C−) of the sharing of tasks denies the claim that the care-giving role is 'unique'.[8] The status awarded to the nurse and her control over the official role of care giver is threatened by this model for care.

Power and control in nursing practice

Beattie and Durguerian[26] described and discussed the colonization of self-help groups such as Family Planning. The introduction of health-care professionals into these groups may result in the application of a problem-solving to care, but not necessarily the full participation of the client group in all aspects of the process.

Any model for practice and a division of labour reflecting weak classification (C−), strong framing (F+) demands a reorientation in the nurse's attitudes towards the value of working in close proximity to doctors and medical technology. Similarly, the model requires a reorientation of the doctor's attitudes towards nurses as his personal assistants.[36] This reorientation of attitudes and the nurse's value system militates against the adoption of models for practice which stress weak classification (C−) (Figures 1 and 2). In the light of a 'codes and control' framework, the control exerted by the nurse as a member of the organization is a major factor in determining the degree to which the patient is allowed to have an active say in the plan of care.[37]

The frameworks presented in Figures 1 and 2 suggest that the control the patient has over the access to the resources of the formal health-care system is a reflection of the limited control the nurse herself has over the resources needed to implement her plan of care. Although the literature on the nursing process perceives the role of the nurse as an independent practitioner, the nurse must defer to her manager for the resources required to implement her plan of care. In the study of the implementation of the nursing process,[11] Keyzer described the manager's control over the decision to implement this mode of practice and the effect the manager's control over essential resources had on the attempt to implement the desired mode of practice. Further, in their arguments against the implementation of the nursing process, individual nurses and groups of nurses described how the degree to which the nursing process was implemented depended on the nurse's perception of the priorities for her time. Similarly, the support the nurse could expect from her manager in the implementation of the nursing process depended on that manager's perception of the priorities for the resources held.[11]

The distribution of power and control over decision-making in the organization is reflected in the power relationships held by the nurse and the patient. In terms of the 'codes and control' framework (Figures 1 and 2), in the hospital setting this may be said to lie along a continuum from strong classification, weak framing (C+, F−) to strong classification, strong framing (C+, F+) (Figures 1 and 2). The power the individual clinical nurse has to redefine her role and that of the patient is limited to the parameters set down by the powerholders. It is unlikely that any model for care which disturbs the existing role boundaries and power structures will be allowed to be implemented by those whose power it seeks to remove.

The conceptual frameworks developed for the study of the implementation of the nursing process[11] are useful in examining the changes required to implement the 'practitioner' role described in the literature on the nursing process. The frameworks draw our attention to the present distribution of power and control within the nursing organization and, hence, the complexity of the changes envisaged by the GNC,[1] the RCN[24] and the UKCC.[2] The traditional power structures and role boundaries have ensured that the clinical nurse and her patient are in positions of relative weakness vis-à-vis the doctor and the nurse manager. This, in turn, has curtailed the development of the role of the clinical nurse and her claim to 'practitioner' status based on technical expertise.

The traditional distribution of power and control has been reinforced by the education programme. The internalization of the power structure as part of the professional socialization of the novice, together with the control exerted by the medical profession over the knowledge base used to guide practice, have maintained the role boundaries between the nurse, the patient, the doctor and the nurse manager. Thus, nurse managers, educationists and doctors have conspired to maintain models for care, in which the division of labour between nurses, and between the roles of the doctor, the nurse and the patient, remain in the status quo of the traditional Nightingale framework.

The data gathered in the study of the implementation of the nursing process,[11] especially that concerned with role conflict, suggested that clinical nurses have only limited power to implement a mode of practice which imbues the role of the clinical nurse with some of the power of decision-making held by the nurse manager and the doctor. An example of how nurses and doctors maintained their role boundaries *vis-à-vis* the patient is recorded in the study.[11] These health-care professionals excluded the patients from the decision-making process in both the psychiatric and general wards.

Further, the care plans created by the nurses employed in the community hospital and the geriatric unit contained no reference to the part played by the patient in defining his needs for care. In contrast to the nurses' claims that they were creating a home for the elderly person, the individual patients had to comply with the bylaws of the hospital. These bylaws inhibited the personal control the individual patient had over such simple daily living needs as access to the world outside the boundaries of the ward and the hospital. One of the nursing innovations recorded in the study concerned the lack of control the patients had over the fate of their personal belongings in the ward. To overcome this problem an individual clothing scheme was initiated by the nurses in the geriatric unit. This innovation was accomplished only with the financial help of the medical profession.[11]

The data recorded in the study[11] suggested that the clinical nurse is ill-prepared for the demands being made of her by nurse leaders.[3] This is caused by an inadequate basic education programme and a limited access to post-basic education. The present education system available to the nurse is, however, itself a reflection of the links between nursing and women's work in general. Thus the education of the nurse is an integral part of a purposeful strategy which maintains the role boundaries between the nurse, the doctor, the manager and, ultimately, the patient.

Towards a theory of nursing: a 'codes and control' model

The conceptual frameworks of 'codes and control' presented in this chapter are useful for examining the changing role of the nurse and the division of labour between the nurse and the patient. A 'codes and control' framework draws our attention to the distribution of power and control within the present nursing organization and the strategies which have kept the clinical nurse and her patient in positions of weakness relative to the power invested in the roles of the doctor and the manager.

The education programmes developed and controlled by the hierarchy and, through the adoption of the medical model, the medical profession, have supported this distribution of power and control through the professional socialization of the student nurse. In this way the traditional training programme is itself part of an overall strategy which maintains the status quo of the hierarchical bureaucracy of the nursing organization.

When applied to the concepts underlying the 'nursing' models presented by Henderson,[8] King,[33] Orem[34] and Roy and Roberts,[30] the 'codes and control' framework indicates the redistribution of power and control between the doctor, the nurse and the patient from that inherent in the traditional model for care in Britain. The processes of nursing contained in these models have different degrees of power-sharing between the nurse and the patient. The model advanced by Henderson continues to stress the physical needs for care and imbues the nurse with greater power than the patient. That proposed by Orem offers a variety of power-sharing relationships based on a contractual nurse—patient relationship. The introduction of either of these models in the United Kingdom could be achieved by assimilating them into the traditional power relationships. The change achieved would, therefore, be more apparent than real. This would still keep the power of decision-making and access to resources firmly in the hands of the doctor, the manager and the nurse. Like the concept of 'total patient care' this strategy would continue the reification of the role of the professional nurse.

The application of the 'codes and control' model to the historical development of the nursing role identifies the debasement of the care-giving aspects in favour of the managerial role. The introduction of a framework for practice which values the previously less favoured role demands a change in the attitudes held by the nurse as well as a reorganization of the workload. This, in turn, demands an organizational climate in which the nurse feels safe to take the risks associated with the implementation of change. Management, therefore, need to support strategies for change in which change agents are identified and helped through open channels of communications. The involvement of all levels of nurse in supplying the resources needed to implement the desired change in practice is central to the degree of success achieved.

Regardless of the 'nursing' model chosen by the clinical nurse, the new power relationships she holds with the patient differ from those in the traditional 'medical' model for care. The changes desired in the clinical role at this point in the development of the nursing profession are an attempt by nurses to redefine the role of the nurse and not an extension of the existing role. If it were a case of role extension then that aspect of the role to be extended would be the managerial and not the clinical role. The role of the nurse in the United Kingdom is that of a manager and not a practitioner. This managerial role is part of the formal structure of the National Health Service. Even the educationists employed in the schools of nursing and midwifery are managers of the education programme, as witnessed by their career structure in the management hierarchy. This does not imply that nurses have no right to a managerial role, or that all nurse managers are necessarily a barrier to the development of the nursing profession. There is, however, evidence that not all nurse managers fulfil their leadership role in the change towards a nursing model in practice and education.[11,32]

The lack of a clear commitment to a policy of continuing education has denied the clinical nurse the opportunity to develop specific clinical expertise to enhance her organizational power, to control her job content and work environment. Thus, the present education programme is part of an organizational strategy in which the managers have conspired with the government and the medical profession to maintain the power structures of the traditional Nightingale organization. Hence the role conflict experienced by the nurses attempting to imbue the clinical role with some of the power over decision-making traditionally belonging to the manager and the doctor.

The 'codes and control' framework offers a theoretical guide to help the nurse to understand the nature of the organization in which she works and provides insights to the implicit and explicit definitions of her role as reflected in her organizational relationships with the doctor, the manager and the patient. By understanding her organizational role more clearly, the nurse is more likely to comprehend the complexities of a change towards a nursing model in practice and education. The existing managerial role of the nurse is implicitly and explicitly stated in the division of labour within the hierarchical bureaucracy of the National Health Service. The uncritical acceptance and application of frameworks for practice which have their origins in another culture and organization of health care, is a source of difficulty where these frameworks challenge the distribution of power and control in society and the organization.[27]

The contribution that a 'codes and control' framework can make towards the creation of a theory of nursing, reflecting care-giving in its social and organizational setting, is to draw attention to the cultural and social factors which determine the traditional role of the nurse within the health-care organization. The framework identifies the need to study the division of labour between the nurse and the woman in her own home and thereby to clarify the role of the patient. An understanding of the cultural concepts of health, illness and care-giving held by the client population is central to the understanding of the role of the nurse and her place in the formal and non-formal care-giving systems available to the patient. Thus an understanding of the role of the patient and the division of labour between the role of the nurse and the woman in her own home could lead to a greater understanding of the type of health-care programme that is both acceptable to and expected by the client population.

Nursing organizations in the future: new opportunities to develop the practitioner role

The United Kingdom Central Council[3] drew attention to the review and critical scrutiny of the nursing service as part of the current reorganization of the National Health Service. The introduction of 'general' managers, some of whom have been recruited from outside the health-care professions, has seriously challenged the power of senior nurse managers. Within Wales the post of Chief Administrative Nursing Officer (CANO) has been retained, but these senior nurses no longer have the same line management relationships with the new Directors of Nursing Services that they once held.

The shift of power within the organization, which has placed control over decision-making in resource allocation in the hands of non-nurses, has come at a time when the profession is seeking to increase its organizational power in the clinical area through the practitioner role. While a great deal of both public and professional attention has been focused on the right of nurses to manage nursing, little debate has taken place on the opportunities available to develop the clinical role.

The restructuring of the nursing services begs the following question: can the role of the practitioner be developed in conjunction with the continuation of the managerial role, or must one be sacrificed for the other? The answer to this question lies in the nurse managers' ability to identify the contributions nurses make to the provision of health care. The vehicle for establishing this falls within the domain of manpower planning. Nurse managers in Wales are approaching this problem through a nurse workload management system.[38]

This system is based on the identification of the client group's needs for care, the numbers and grade of nursing staff required to meet those needs and, through this, the demand and supply of nurses in the future. It is envisaged that current ongoing work in Wales will eventually create a more accurate method of determining the grade and skill mix of staff required to meet a specific population's needs for care in both the hospital and community setting. An opportunity therefore exists for nurses to take the lead in planning the future structure and role of the nursing service, through a greater awareness of the contribution each level of nurse brings to patient care. Beginnings undoubtably have implications for the future and it may well be that the legacy of the past will influence the development of the nursing service.

There is, however, a growing body of research-based knowledge on which nurses, at all levels, can draw to support decision-making, a greater access to continuing, higher education than in the past and an awareness amongst nurses of the more global factors which determine their role and status within society and the organization. The challenge to nurses in the future is one of leadership. The original Nightingale nurse had a clear role in bringing about social change in the provision of health care. This role may have received less attention than it deserved in the intervening years, but it still exists.

To secure the future education of the nurse and the practitioner role as envisaged by the United Kingdom Central Council[3] there must be unity within the profession. In the past, the lack of unity within the profession has been one of the factors influencing the present preparation for and role of the nurse. In determining their future in this period of social and organizational change, nurses must overcome their differences based on boundary maintenance and renew the leadership role they once held in promoting the wellbeing of individuals and social groups. Failure to grasp the opportunity to change the education of the nurse could result in past practices being retained, to the detriment of the profession and the public.

References

1. General Nursing Council for England and Wales, GNC Education Policy, 1977, Ref. 77/19/A, HMSO, London, 1977.

2. United Kingdom Central Council for Nursing, Midwifery and Health Visiting, 'Education and Training', Working Group 3, Consultation Paper 1, UKCC, London, 1982.
3. United Kingdom Central Council for Nursing, Midwifery and Health Visiting, 'Project 2000: A new preparation for practice', UKCC, London, 1986.
4. Ashworth, P., Castledine, G. and McFarlane, J. K., 'The process in practice', Nursing Times Supplement, 1978, 30 November, 3–4.
5. Webb, C., 'Classification and framing: a sociological analysis of task-centred nursing and the nursing process', Journal of Advanced Nursing, 1981, 6, 369–376.
6. Clark, J., 'Putting the patient first', Nursing Times, 1985, 81, No. 7, 22.
7. Holmes, P., 'Celebrating the process', Nursing Times, 1985, 81, No. 4, 20.
8. Henderson, V., The Nature of Nursing. Collier-Macmillan, London, 1966.
9. Wright, S., 'A rich experience', Nursing Times, 1985, 81, No. 36, 37–38.
10. Aggleton, P. and Chalmers, H., 'Henderson's Model', Nursing Times, 1985, 81, No. 10, 33–35.
11. Keyzer, D. M., Learning Contracts, The Trained Nurse and the Implementation of the Nursing Process: Comparative Case Studies in the Management of Knowledge and Change in Nursing Practice, PhD thesis, London University Institute of Education, 1985. (a) p. 67; (b) p. 68; (c) p. 72; (d) p. 185; (e) 168.
12. Maggs, C., 'The state of the art', Nursing Times, 1985, 81, No. 24, 36.
13. Summers, A., 'Just what did the nurses do?' Nursing Times, 1985, 81, No. 13, 43–45.
14. Storr, F., 'The benevolent Ladies of Gloucester', Nursing Times, 1985, 81, No. 9, 41.
15. Davies, C., 'Experience of dependency and control in work: the case of nurses', Journal of Advanced Nursing, 1976, 1, 273–282.
16. Davies, C., 'Comparative occupational roles in health care', Social Science and Medicine, 1979, 13A, 515–521.
17. Davies, C., 'Continuities in the development of hospital nursing in Britain', Journal of Advanced Nursing, 1977, 2, 479–493.
18. Bygraves, D., 'Whose job is it, anyway?' Nursing Times, 1985, 81, No. 19, 52.
19. Greenleaf, N. P., 'The politics of self esteem', Nursing Digest, 1978, VI, No. 3, 1–9.
20. Dingwall, R. and McIntosh, J., Readings in the Sociology of Nursing. Churchill Livingstone, Edinburgh, 1978, pp. 19–35.
21. Abel-Smith, B., A History of the Nursing Profession. Heinemann, London, 1960.
22. Salmon Report, The Report of the Committee on Senior Nursing Staff Structure. Ministry of Health and Scottish Home and Health Department (Chairman B. Salmon), HMSO, London, 1966.
23. Davies, C., Rewriting Nursing History. Croom Helm, London, 1980.
24. Royal College of Nursing, 'A Structure for Nursing', RCN, London, 1981.
25. Bernstein, B., Class, Codes and Control, vol. 1, Theoretical Studies Towards a Sociology of Language. Routledge & Kegan Paul, London, 1975.

26. Beattie, A. and Durguerian, S., *Organisations, Occupations and Ideologies in Family Planning: A Case Study in the Sociology of Knowledge*. Unpublished paper, London University Institute of Education, 1980.
27. Keyzer, D. M., 'Concepts of care: a way of life', *Nursing Practice*, 1986, **1**, 190–195.
28. White, R., 'Educational entry requirements for nurse registration: an historical perspective', *Journal of Advanced Nursing*, 1985, **10**, 583–590.
29. De La Cuesta, 'The nursing process: from development to implementation', *Journal of Advanced Nursing*, 1983, **8**, 365–371.
30. Roy Sr. C. and Roberts, S. L., *Theory Construction in Nursing: An Adaptation Model*. Prentice Hall, London, 1981.
31. Bendall, E., *So you passed, nurse?* Royal College of Nursing, London, 1975.
32. Hollingworth, S., *Preparation for change*, RCN, London, 1985.
33. King, I. M., *Towards a Theory for Nursing*. John Wiley, Chichester, 1971.
34. Orem, D. E., *Nursing: Concepts of Practice*, 2nd edition. McGraw-Hill, New York, 1980.
35. Tuckett, D., *An Introduction to Medical Sociology*. Tavistock Publications, London, 1977.
36. Anderson, E. R., *The Role of the Nurse*. Royal College of Nursing, London, 1973.
37. Stacey, M., Dearden, R., Pill, R. and Robinson, D., *Hospitals, Children and their Families*. Routledge & Kegan Paul, London, 1970.
38. Welsh Office, First Report of the All Wales Nurse Manpower Planning Committee (WHC 85/32), 1985.

Political Issues in Nursing: Past, Present and Future, Volume 3
Edited by R. White
© 1988 John Wiley & Sons Ltd

CHAPTER 7

Women's health: a nursing perspective

JEAN ORR, MSc, BA, RGN, RHV
Lecturer in Nursing, University of Manchester, Manchester, England

Introduction

There has been little emphasis on the issue of women's health within the National Health Service[1] in general and within nursing in particular.[2] Where there are distinct facilities, these are related to the reproductive functions of women in gynaecology and midwifery. However, even in these areas, where it could be expected that women would be given sympathetic care, this is not always the case.[3]

Women's needs are not being met or acknowledged throughout other areas of health care and, indeed, the way patients are labelled may hide the fact that there could be a nursing perspective which focused on women. This is apparent in the field of nursing elderly people where, in reality, most of the patients are in fact women. Health Visitors, while in theory working with the family, are mainly involved with women. District Nurses have a major role in nursing women in the home and supporting women carers who form the mainstay of community care.[4] Family Planning Clinics are attended by women; elderly women suffer fractures and so are hospitalized in orthopaedic wards.

The rate of depression in women, and the rate at which they seek professional help, is twice that of men, and married women have higher rates of depression than single, widowed or divorced women and men. Therefore psychiatric nurses have contact with many vulnerable women but female patients are treated with less seriousness than men.[5]

Nurses, as women, have considerable health problems and as a group, have a disproportionately high mortality rate compared with a number of other professions and occupations and, especially, when compared with other female-dominated professions such as teaching.[6] By comparison the number of suicides and suicide-related causes of death is alarmingly high. Hinckley further states that stress and stress-related factors may be an important influence in determining morbidity, absence and wastage levels within the nursing profession. Nurses have been found to cope with stress by smoking, taking alcohol and caffeine.

It would seem therefore, that the health of women is of concern for nurses as providers and consumers of the National Health Service and we must question why so little importance has been given to it within nursing. The ways in which disciplines are thought about, and debate within disciplines, are not just structures of thought but are structures of power.[7] Therefore, definitions of women's health, theories of illness, attitudes to sexuality, nursing routines, research methods, views of language or procedures for the organization of work are all conceptual systems defining the pattern of domination of a given culture and period in history. What is included and what is excluded in an area of study are as important as the way the field of study is organized and presented to the world. Those who organize and control a system such as health care also formulate the values which underpin it. Debates about health care must focus not only on the way the services are operated but also on how health, nursing and medicine are defined. In general, nursing like medicine is seen as primarily curative rather than preventive and as a response to illness and injury, focusing on sickness rather than health. The current proposals in Project 2000[8] go some way to challenge this traditional definition, but it is likely to take a considerable time before nursing will move to a health model. The influence of medicine on hospital nursing will make any such shift difficult, as nursing is seen as an adjunct to medicine, despite the increasing striving for a separate professional identity. If nurses are actively to play a part in health-care policies, they must be knowledgeable about the shortcomings of the service.

Current issues

Critique of health-care policy

Within the critique of health-care policy there are four main themes. Firstly, it is argued that doctors have medicalized a range of life experiences from childbirth to old age, so that doctors now have a claim to intervention which is difficult for patients or other workers, such as nurses, to challenge.[9] By defining the situations as pathological any other interpretation is excluded. For example, if depression in women was seen as a result of powerlessness, tranquillizers would be inappropriate, drug companies would suffer and doctors would be unnecessary. It is obviously in the medical lobby's interest not to support any such social definition.

Secondly, there is an increase in the use of medical technology which is said to alienate patients from their bodies and raise the status of those who use such machines.[10] Access to knowledge of this technology is restricted and nurses, for example, are excluded from taking part in high-status treatment. Thirdly, the division in health care reflects the sexual division of labour that exists in all other areas of life.[11] Doctors are predominately male and involved in scientific procedures, while nurses are predominately female and concerned with caring, which is seen as low-status and women's natural work. This may be why men in nursing go into management and teaching as quickly as possible in order to distance themselves from 'naturally' female work.

Fourthly, health care is seen as a means of social control and intent on maintaining the dominant position of men in society. Although many people do not see health care as an instrument of social control and a disseminator of patriarchal values, an increasing body of feminist literature would suggest that it is both.[12,13]

Nurses do not escape from the feminist critique. Daly[14] argues that nurses are employed as 'token torturers' to carry out painful and destructive treatment. It is nurses, she argues, who give injections and it is they who withhold pain medication. 'Programmed not to answer women's questions they sometimes magnify suffering by unreasonable silence and degrading non-answers.' Nurses perform procedures which are painful such as changing dressings after surgery, and this is when the patient is awake. The doctors perform the deepest wounding when the patient is under anaesthesia. Therefore, most procedures experienced as painful are done by women, whereas the doctors' actions, which may be extremely harmful, are not directly seen as such.

This is not a comfortable analysis for many nurses but it does have some credence if we apply the argument. For example, while health visitors are involved in the identification and procedures in case conferences of parents suspected of child abuse, many general practitioners remain in the background, not wishing to damage the relationship with the family. Parents know that health visitors and social workers are key agents in child abuse; general practitioners are not. And yet, the doctor is seen as 'owning' the family and nurses must be 'attached' to gain status.

Daly sees the nurse as 'both weapon and shield for the divine doctor in his warfare against disease to which the woman as patient is susceptible by her nature'. This idea that female function is inherently pathological is one that can be identified throughout health care, be it puberty, menstruation, pregnancy or menopause. These are seen as 'medical conditions' by doctors and treated as such, while to women they are part of life. Much of the early treatment of women's illnesses focused on restricting women's lives and preventing them from competing in the outside world of men. If women's reproductive function is seen as sickness, all sickness in women is often seen as a result of normal reproductive functioning. Therefore women are consistently told that illness is due to their age, be that 14 or 40. It is little wonder that women have been less than satisfied with health care.

Ungerson,[15] while recognizing these criticisms, goes on to point out that the health-care system is also a resource. The way in which access to that resource is organized and financed is the crucial issue for women. It is also a crucial issue for nurses if they want to influence health policies. The issue focuses on the wider debate about power in society and the role of health care in alleviating inequalities in society. Nurses working with individuals and family may be confronted with evidence of inequality or poverty, but at the individual level the issue is quite dissipated and not very threatening. Therefore nurses may recognize that unemployment has an effect on health but decide there is little they can do.

It is often implied, or argued, in social and health services that helping individuals in need is not a political act. While it is not exclusively so, it is nevertheless based on an implied or explicit commitment to how the world is, or should be. The nature of nursing activities and their consequences have effects which are political.[16] They may confirm or challenge the existing distribution of power, the allocation of resources and dominant value system. Nursing takes place within a context that is essentially political. After all, nurses are public employees carrying out government policy. The daily decisions about practice and priorities derive not from neutral principles based on objective truths but from political interpretations of the world and identifiable political purposes. There is a naïve belief that it is only activists from the left or right who are political. Those who support the existing system rarely see this commitment as political or recognize the inherent militancy of their position. This is particularly pertinent when the nature of health care changes, as it is doing with economic constraints. In this situation the role of the professional becomes more controlling in allowing access to scarce resources. The political and repressive features of health care become more evident, and professionals are faced with policies which are based on ideas of efficiency and cost effectiveness and seek short-term benefits to meet economic targets, often using epidemiological evidence to support the policies.

Epidemiology

Nurses working in hospital and community are increasingly taught to adopt an epidemiological approach to defining health problems and setting priorities for intervention. This approach means that intervention is called for when the condition is significant, that is, when it causes considerable mortality or severe morbidity and affects large populations.

Successful or effective services are often so measured in terms of 'cures', or 'positives' in a screening programme. Such simple criteria might be appropriate if it were equally legitimate to give the same value to all members of the community. We do not in fact do this; for instance, it is often assumed that the best interests of society are served by providing services to maintain the 'working population' at work: it is argued that we depend economically on these productive members. What, however, does such a statement tell us about the implicit value attached to one such member of the community relative to, say, a retired man, or a woman working in the home, rather than for an employer?

Programmes, therefore, tend to focus on high-status, high-earning groups and so there are programmes which aim to prevent heart disease in upper-income men and few programmes which focus on smoking in working-class women. This lack of value on women's contribution to the economy, in its widest sense, is all the more worrying when the increasing burden of community care is going to fall on women. Hull[17] approaches the issue by asking about the cost of replacing the contribution made by a woman who dies early. What is the cost to society of alternative care for the children, support for the husband, the cost of hospitalizing the elderly relative living with the family and nursed by the wife, and the cost of some other means of support for the disabled neighbour next door? The network of care and support that is so often the daily routine of many 'non-working' wives is extensive and so very often quite taken for granted until the day when the wife is herself ill and the whole system collapses. Although a woman's contribution cannot be conveniently measured in terms of working days lost, any such superficial examination suggests that her value is enormous.

Feminist epidemiological studies are beginning to make visible the causes of ill health in women.[18] The predominance of men, that is male occupations, in offical statistics and the lack of documentation of female occupations, has resulted in a failure to recognize and direct preventive strategy to the occupational health needs of women. This skewing of statistics in favour of men serves to reinforce the stereotype of women as housewives at a time when, in fact, 50 per cent of women with dependent children are working outside the home. Such problems as dysmenorrhoea due to occupation, infections, sexual harassment and chemical/radiation hazards are now being documented. Also, health problems of women in the private arena are being highlighted, that is the preponderance of violence and accidents suffered by women in the home. Feminist health researchers are also compiling a critique of the NHS and other related agencies. They highlight that the difficulties of obtaining data on rape, violence and so on are due, in part, to the reluctance of women victims to utilize the service of agencies and staff whose behaviour reflects patriarchal social mores.[19]

At the same time as the male scientific view of health and disease invades every event of life, there is a general dispossession of motherhood knowledge. So that mother's knowledge, learnt from experience, observation and older women, is considered obsolete. This results in increased anxiety and guilt, loss of self-confidence, dependency and ignorance.[20] Feeling unable to learn by themselves, mothers lose the ability to build up their self-awareness and become anxious lest they have done something harmful to their children. They are unprepared to face any small difficulty or obstacle such as bad colds, sore ears, slight vomiting or stomach ache. Having lost their own references and the ability to use them properly and feeling they might do wrong, they develop a sense of guilt, show no self-confidence and therefore build up a very poor image of themselves. In this way women become more and more passive and dependent on men's advice. They rely on doctors, psychologists, psychoanalysts or on their advice transferred to them through professionalized women, such as health visitors or nurses. The effect of this might reach complete absence of any kind of understanding and knowledge.

Most health visitors could draw on examples of this when mothers follow advice to extremes. For example, when one mother was told to give her baby carrots she did so at every feed and the child became ill and jaundiced. Within health visiting there is also the view that the advice given by grannies or other female family members has to be negated and student health visitors frequently write about the problems of contradicting such advice, which is not scientific and proven, that is, recorded within journals and books.

Feminist writers are concerned with the disparity between the traditional view of health, as evidenced in medical and scientific writings, and their own and other women's experience of what it is to be healthy women.[21] Much of the feminist literature has attempted to define women's health by drawing on the experiences of women and seeing these experiences as valid data.[22] We can draw comparisons here between this approach, as it involves women, and the lay self-help movement, which has as its central tenet the belief that persons who have experienced a health problem have an understanding of that condition which those without do not fully comprehend.

Within health care, clinical knowledge often goes against the personal experiences of women, but it is the professional knowledge which is deemed to be correct, because of the difference in status and power. Women are socialized into believing that their own intuitive knowledge is not as credible as that of a professional. It is within the field of obstetrics that this conflict can be easily seen. Oakley[23] quotes an example from an antenatal clinic which highlights how the male doctor is thought to be an expert on having a baby.

MALE DOCTOR: 'Will you keep a note in your diary of when you first feel the baby move?'

PATIENT: 'Do you know—well of course you would know—what it feels like?'

MALE DOCTOR: 'It feels like wind pains—something moving in your tummy.'

The predominance of male medical/quantitative analysis of health is being challenged. Although men's health is deemed to be poorer than women's, since men figure predominantly in mortality statistics, feminist qualitative analysis raises questions as to the meaning of health and illness: while the feminist perspective acknowledges that men's lives are short and brutal, it also reveals that women's lives are long and miserable.[24]

We are now beginning to see the causes of women's ill health as often related to the very heavy burden they carry in caring for the family, or to being a member of a violent family, or to poor working conditions. Nurses need to be aware that significant health problems of women are often related to the social, psychological and structural factors in women's lives. Therefore we must question the labelling of women which takes place in health care when women, for example, are blamed for being the victims of violence. This is an important area for nurses, both as potential victims and helpers, as it is estimated that one in four women will have experienced sexual abuse[25] and one in ten will experience violence.[26] A study by Stark[27] showed that battered women had three times as many abortions and twice as many miscarriages as other women. Battered women were far more likely to be pregnant when injured, and kicking pregnant women in the abdomen has been described. This has obvious implications for midwives and health visitors. Nurses should suspect abuse when a woman has multiple injuries, when she is injured while pregnant or has a history of multiple or self-induced abortions, and when she reports persistent or vague medical complaints, has attempted suicide, has persistently used tranquillizers, or is anxious and depressed. There are implications for nurses working in psychiatric hospitals. Women who have been abused make multiple visits to medical and psychiatric services for general health problems which superficially appear to be unrelated to abuse, but which are as much a part of the battering syndrome as the physical injury.

There are three suggested stages of battering. In the first stage are those women who have suffered repeated physical injury and minor medical or mental complaints. Those in the second stage present with physical injuries accompanied by more serious psychosocial problems, and so they are referred to psychiatrists. Women in the third stage have made multiple suicide attempts and present with severe medical or mental health problems. Abuse at this third stage often turns to self-abuse, and helpers see the symptoms as the cause of abuse rather than as the result. In other words, because the woman has severe mental health problems we can see why she might be battered. Many battered women at this stage are sent to psychiatric hospitals and day centres, where the approach is often to reinforce traditional female stereotypes. Putting on make-up and doing housework are seen as signs of recovery, and are the price to be paid for being 'cured'.

Much of the non-recognition of abuse is based on the model of care we deliver and the political biases we exhibit in defining need and allocating resources. The woman is seen as the problem for the family and not as the product of it. Battering should be part of the differential diagnosis that nurses make, for the woman may be reluctant to state the problem overtly because of the stigma involved. Women who are victims of any form of male violence may be reluctant to be nursed by male nurses or to be in a mixed ward, but this is one area of patient choice which is not addressed.

The nurse's role in women's health care

Nurses can play a key role in shaping health-care policies for women, policies which should benefit nurses as clients and patients because, after all, nurses are also the recipients of the service. There are four possible ways forward. Firstly, nurses need to recognize the political forces which determine 'health' as it applies particularly to women. The womens' health movement has emphasized and articulated the effects of social, economic and cultural forces on health-care services and health, and has stressed that health, while being personal, is also political.[3] For example, the woman who cares for a handicapped, elderly or dependent relative may become stressed and exhausted because there is little help from social or health services. Indeed it may be that the woman is given no choice in caring for the relative, even if this means her losing her long-term security in terms of pension rights and job prospects. Her commitment to the family is personal, the context is political.

Secondly, nurses can help women to define health problems and work out solutions which are acceptable and appropriate. Allied to this is the idea of helping women determine what they want from the health services. Frequently, women put the welfare of other members of the family before themselves and will often feed the family but not themselves. Women experience a conflict between their self-interest and their allegiance to family.

It is in the area of reproduction and fertility that women need to be helped to determine what they want in terms of obstetric care and to be offered information from which they can make informed choice. Midwives could be more active in ensuring that women in the antenatal clinics are not treated as badly as they are in many areas of the country, and kept waiting unnecessarily at the convenience of the doctor.[28] There is considerable criticism of antenatal care but little evidence that changes are taking place. Many midwives refuse to challenge the medical hierarchy and, indeed, collude with the dominant value system dividing women into the respectable married and the unmarried, thus defining the woman, not in relation to her unborn child, but in her relationship with a man. Horror stories abound in health care, and the above point was reinforced by a colleague at an antenatal clinic who heard the midwife shout to the assembled room of pregnant women, 'Those who aren't married come through here'.[29] The pity was that all of the women did not rise up and confuse the system.

It is not only in hospital that nurses can help women. Much of health promotion and prevention is presented to women as prescriptive and punitive, and takes no account of the context of women's lives. If we take the example of smoking, it has been shown that women are a prime target of the tobacco industry, explicitly because they live longer and so smoke more, they are less successful at stopping than men, they are earning money to spend on cigarettes and they are suffering from pressures at work and at home which encourage smoking. In addition, women are persuaded to buy cigarettes by special cut-price offers at supermarkets, by advertising in women's and teenage girls' magazines and by the introduction of especially feminine long-slim cigarettes. This sex-specific marketing has researched the situation thoroughly. The health promoters have not. The advice given to women on stopping smoking is based on the reasons why men smoke and does not address the fact that women smoke because of stress related to their lives as women. Jacobson[30] records the voices of women describing their dependence on tobacco and how it soothes the aggression and stress and yet acts as a stimulant whenever exhaustion or boredom sets in. Cigarettes seem to help with the stress of demanding families, lack of autonomy at work and with not getting fat. In addition, it seems women buy themselves cigarettes as an acceptable treat. Therefore, in order to stop women smoking, these factors have to be taken into account and the main approach of the nurse must be to help raise women's self-esteem and help them to see themselves as valuable.

Thirdly, nurses must recognize the contribution women make in the caring and nurturing roles undertaken within health care itself and in the wider society. The health-care system depends on this social support and care which is given by women (be they nurses or clients) but affords little recognition of either. Care is seen as women's work and therefore of lesser worth than the male work of treatment. An analysis of aspects of care, as it relates to women, suggests that nurses need to rehabilitate it and make it visible by demonstrating the wide difference between care, cure and treatment, and to prove its indispensability. It is argued that it is possible to live without treatment but it is not possible to live without care.[20] This would appear to be particularly true when caring for patients for whom there is no treatment such as the terminally ill, the chronically handicapped or those with AIDS.

Fourthly, nurses need critically to examine the move to participation with the users of health care. This is becoming a central issue as the concern about the cost of health care increases and the shift of care to the community intensifies. It is possible to argue that policy-makers are embracing participation in an attempt to stem public concern about limited community care provision and in order to utilize the range of voluntary, self-help and lay networks. Participation is related most frequently to the arena of community health, removed as it is from the high-status world of hospital care. It is noticeable that the power relationships within hospitals have not been challenged by any move to involve patients or potential patients in decision-making or the planning of care.

Recent trends in primary health care have been to involve the clients and community in the planning and delivery of health care. This makes explicit a shift in the relationship between the nurses and the community. It is envisaged that local people will be encouraged by nurses to take a more active role in health-care issues. For example, in 1974[31] the World Health Organization defined community nursing not only as including family-health nursing but as also being concerned with identifying the community's broad health needs and involving the community in development projects related to health and welfare. Community nursing is said to be involved in helping communities to identify their own problems, to find solutions and to take such actions as they can before calling on outside assistance.

Within the WHO there has been a gradual shift of emphasis in primary health care to include the recipients of care in planning. The changes in public and professional opinion were set forth in the Declaration of Alma Ata.[32] They can be summarized under four headings:

(1) health care should be related to the needs of the population;
(2) consumers should participate, both individually and collectively, in the planning and implementation of health care;
(3) the fullest use must be made of available resources; and
(4) primary health care is not an isolated approach but the most local part of a comprehensive health system.

This emphasis on participation was also evident in the report of a WHO workshop on Nursing and Primary Health Care held in Manilla.[33] At this workshop it was stressed that the nurse should play a very different role from that undertaken at present and needs a different range of skills and knowledge, which would help the nurses to be facilitators, educate community workers, support workers and participate in evaluating community programmes.

More recently, the report of the *Review of Community Nursing*[34] states that the starting point for services should be peoples' needs rather than professional aspirations and that existing services are failing to identify systematically the needs of many people in the community. The report also stresses that primary health care services should enable people to make decisions about their health on the basis of informed choice and involve partnership with and support for carers, involve all disciplines and statutory and voluntary agencies and ensure that the planning and evaluation of services involve people in the community as well as health professionals. While rhetoric about participation and client involvement is welcomed, there is little debate about how this might be achieved and the change in approach which will be necessary.

To work with women in the community, nurses have to be prepared to change much of the existing client/professional relationship and means of service delivery. There are many innovatory schemes operating through the United Kingdom, some of which are described in the Report of the Working Group on *Women and the Health Service*.[35] There is no doubt that women are a major force in the community health movement which is a growing and distinct part of health provision in Britain. This movement is said to be based outside the health professionals and is concerned with inequalities in health and health-care provision.[36] It is based on the belief that the achievement of a healthy community depends on a collective awareness of the social causes of ill health and positive health and is concerned to challenge, at an individual and collective level, the monopoly of information about health and ill health held by health professionals.

The fact that women themselves are organizing is indicative of their concern and their determination to bring about change. The women's health movements are a good example of how women have challenged the health-care professionals and have spearheaded a nationwide movement.[37] In the north-west of England, for example, there is a strong, articulate body of women who have succeeded in setting up women's health classes and self-help groups and have thus been instrumental in changing policy and establishing well women clinics. While these women are from very diverse backgrounds, they appear united in their demand for health care on their terms.

The well women clinics which have been set up are examples of how lay and professional women have influenced policies and provided a very different service from that of a cytology or family planning clinic. The emphasis is on helping the women to identify their own health and social needs by taking a holistic approach. Women's health needs, after all, involve more than cervical smears and breast examinations. The women are invited to join a range of self-help groups and attend sessions on health problems such as depression.

The well women clinics are examples of the move to partnership and reflect much of the current rhetoric about health care. They are:

(1) concerned with prevention;
(2) meeting local and articulated needs;
(3) involving local communities and forming partnerships;
(4) using voluntary and lay helpers;
(5) based on a self-help ethos;
(6) reaching clients not covered by existing services;
(7) bringing together a range of disciplines;
(8) taking a holistic approach to care.

The holistic approach to health care refers to a qualitatively different approach, one that respects the interaction of mind, body and environment. Ferguson[38] describes the assumption of the holistic approach and this is similar to the philosophy of well women clinics.

Holistic care is said among other things to: be concerned with the whole person; see the person as autonomous; focus primarily on qualitative information including the person's subjective reports and professionals' intuition. The women are involved in determining their own health needs and every effort is made to demystify health and medical practice. This involves, amongst other things, teaching women about their bodies in order to explain procedures, showing them how to test urine or explaining what blood pressure measurement means. The emphasis in the well women clinics is on partnership between the workers and the clients. The three clinics in the Manchester area vary according to local needs and staff. They are, however, involved in training programmes for all workers and there is an emphasis on sharing skills and knowledge. The clinics are non-hierarchical in organization with all decisions being made at monthly policy meetings. This means that all workers participate and have an involvement in evaluating and developing the clinic outside any rigid bureaucratic models. The professional workers do not have automatic authority because of their specialized knowledge. The clinics are therefore a reflection of what the local women want, and this is made evident by the way the clinics are used and the high degree of satisfaction expressed by users.

An evaluation of the Wythenshawe clinic showed that the original aims of the clinic were met.[39] The clinic aimed:

(1) to reach women who normally stay away from doctors for reasons of class, culture or sex of the doctor;
(2) to try to find effective ways of meeting women's specific health problems;
(3) to develop general understanding about health and health-care provision and the obstacles to their improvement both within the medical profession and in the community so that services and information which will contribute to the good health of the individual and the community can be offered and accepted.

The main target group was defined as women who rarely if ever visit their doctor and who are believed medically to be most at risk, that is the disadvantaged, the poor, the infertile and older women.

Three aspects were noted regarding the problems with which women presented and which were identified at the clinic. First, quite simply, the number of problems, and one in six of the women had at least five. Second, of these problems, less than a third were receiving attention elsewhere, hence most had previously gone untreated. Third, the complexity of these problems was noteworthy. Results indicated that in approximately two-thirds of all cases problems of a different nature— medical, psychological and social or relating to stress—were found to coexist. Attenders were attempting to come to terms with a nexus of problems. Clinic staff aimed to help them unravel their difficulties, which frequently overlapped. For example, reported psychological disorders were more commonly being treated than 'specifically female' ones. Treatment consisted, in the main, of tranquillizers and sleeping tablets. It may well be that this treatment was in some way masking any gynaecological problems which were also present.

Overall, there was evidence of a substantial rate of pathology— both medical and psychological. A third of all women reported marital problems, a third had family problems, two-thirds acknowledged some sleep disturbance and a similar proportion indicated sexual difficulties. A quarter said they felt isolated or lonely. A large number of minor physical problems (such as backache, cough and constipation) were also identified and over half the women had three or more of these. Symptoms associated with menstrual periods or the menopause were also common. Smoking or drinking was a great problem among attenders; there was evidence that, for many, diet was inadequate. Attenders expressed a relatively high level of interest in preventive measures such as giving up smoking, examining their breasts and weight reduction. This was an encouraging indication of the possible reception that would be given to self-help groups and health education.

Over a half of all attenders reported a vaginal discharge and other gynaecological symptoms which were instrumental in bringing them to the clinic. It does seem as if there was a high level of gynaecological disorder which caused concern to the women involved, but which nonetheless went untreated. Nearly a third of women having their first smear presented with some gynaecological disorder, demonstrating that numbers of women were using as a diagnostic service facilities intended as a population screening programme. This can be looked on either as abuse of the service or evidence of an unanswered need amongst the general female population: where else could these women go? All the evidence shows that the present alternatives are unsatisfactory. Treatment at a clinic for sexually transmitted diseases is usually very efficient and can be obtained directly without reference from the general practitioner, but it is apparent that many women do not see these clinics as appropriate for them, or that the stigma attached to them is too great a barrier. A more obvious alternative is treatment either by the GP or at a hospital after GP referral. However, for what are commonly perceived as 'minor women's ailments', this course of action is not considered by either the women or their general practitioners. GPs often feel that they have neither the time nor the expertise to deal with these problems and there have been reports of such difficulties being referred to family planning clinics. It is inefficient and wasteful of scarce resources that these problems should be dealt with by specialized cytological screening services. This situation highlights a very real gap in current services and our evaluation shows that well women clinics are one effective solution to this problem.

One important difference was observed between the expected working of the clinic and the function which it eventually turned out to serve. A great deal of emphasis had been placed in the planning stages on prevention, but attenders came with a great many problems already established. At first sight this curative aspect of the care being given seemed to negate the original goals of the service. However, on closer analysis, this was not necessarily the case. Women certainly were not coming for screening alone but were, in the event, more than happy to be able to make use of the general check-up and screening facilities which were offered to them, in addition to help with their particular problems. They themselves recognized that any one problem did not exist in isolation but had to be considered within the context of the rest of their lives. This awareness made them open to advice about aspects of their life-style not directly connected with their specific difficulties at the time. There is a conclusion to be drawn from these observations: prevention is most effective when offered in conjunction with a service which responds to the self-perceived needs of its clients. This is, perhaps, a valuable lesson which nurses, particularly community nurses, can learn from the Women's Health Movement.

References

1. Phillips, A. and Rakusen, J., *Our Bodies Ourselves: A Health Book By and For Women*. Boston Women's Health Book Collective, Penguin, Harmondsworth, 1978.
2. Orr, J., 'Health visiting and feminism', *Health Visitor*, 1981, **54**, No. 4, 156–157.
3. Leeson, J. and Gray, J., *Women and Medicine*. Tavistock, London, 1978.
4. Dunnell, K. and Dobbs, J., *Nurses Working in the Community*. HMSO, London, 1982.
5. Hamel-Bissel, H., 'For her own good', *Nursing Times*, 1987, 11 February, 44–46.
6. Hinckley, P., *Stress in Nursing*. Kings Fund, London, 1986.
7. Foucault, M., *The History of Sexuality*. Translated by Robert Hurley, Pantheon, New York, 1978.
8. Project 2000, The United Kingdom Central Council for Nursing, Midwifery and Health Visiting, 23 Portland Place, London, 1986.
9. Lewin, E. and Olesen, V., *Womens' Health and Healing: Towards a New Perspective*. Tavistock, London, 1985.
10. The Brighton Women and Science Group. 'Technology in the Lying-in Room'. In The Brighton Women and Science Group (eds), *Alice through the Microscope. The Power of Science over Women's Lives*. Virago, London, 1980.
11. Stacey, M. (ed.), *Health and the Division of Labour*. Croom Helm, London, 1977.
12. Rich, A., *Of Women Born*. Virago, London, 1977.
13. Kjervik, D. and Martinson, J., *Women in Stress: A Nursing Perspective*. Appleton-Century-Crofts, New York, 1979.
14. Daly, M., *Gyn/ecology*. The Womens Press, London, 1979, p. 277.
15. Ungerson, C., *Women and Social Policy*. Macmillan, London, 1985.
16. Orr, J., 'Health visiting and the community'. In Luker, K. and Orr, J. (eds), *Health Visiting*. Blackwell Scientific, Oxford, 1986.
17. Hull, W., 'Economic aspects of womens health'. In Orr, J. (ed.), *Women's Health in the Community*. John Wiley, Chichester, 1987.
18. O'Connor, M., 'Health/illness in healing/caring: a feminist perspective'.

In Orr, J. (ed.), *Women's Health in the Community*. John Wiley, Chichester, 1987.
19. Doyal, L. with Pennell, I., *The Political Economy of Health*. Pluto Press, London, 1979.
20. Colliére, M. T. F., 'Invisible care and invisible women as health care providers', *International Journal of Nursing Studies*, 1986, **23**, No. 2, 95–112.
21. Williams, A., 'Making sense of feminist contributions to women's health'. In Orr, J. (ed.), *Women's Health in the Community*. John Wiley, Chichester, 1987.
22. Ruzek, S. and Hill, J., 'Promoting women's health: redefining the knowledge base and strategies for change', *Health Promotion*, 1986, **1**, No. 3, 301–311.
23. Oakley, A., *Women Confined*. Martin Robertson, London, 1980, p. 15.
24. Hart, N., 'Explaining health inequality between the sexes', *Radical Community Medicine*, 1982, **11**, No. 2, 25–34.
25. Stanko, E., *Intimate Intrusions: Women's Experience of Male Violence*. Routledge & Kegan Paul, London, 1985.
26. Borkowski, M., Murch, M. and Walker, V., *Marital Violence*. Tavistock, London, 1983.
27. Stark, J., *Psychiatric Perspectives on the Abuse of Women*. Centre for Health Studies, Yale University, 1974.
28. Kirkham, M., 'A feminist perspective in midwifery'. In Webb, C. (ed.), *Feminist Practice in Women's Health Care*. John Wiley, Chichester, 1986.
29. Personal communication with M. McWilliams (1986).
30. Jacobson, B., *Beating the Lady Killers*. Pluto Press, London, 1986.
31. World Health Organization 'Community Nursing'. WHO, Geneva, 1974.
32. World Health Organization, 'Primary Health Care'. WHO, Geneva, 1978.
33. World Health Organization, Regional Workshop on Nursing and Midwifery Personnel in Primary Health Care. WHO, Manila, 1979.
34. Report of the Review of Community Nursing (Chairman Mrs Julia Cumberlege) *Neighbourhood Nursing: A Focus for Care*. HMSO, London, 1986.
35. Women's National Commission Report, 'Women and the health service'. WNC Cabinet Offices, London, 1984.
36. Rosenthal, H., 'Neighbourhood health projects', *Community Development Journal*, 1983, **18**, No. 2, 120–131.
37. Orr, J. (ed.), 'Introduction'. In *Women's Health in the Community*. John Wiley, Chichester, 1987.
38. Ferguson, M., *The Aquarian Conspiracy. Personal and Social Transformation in the 1980s*. Granada, London, 1982.
39. Well Women Clinic, *Evaluation Document*. Manchester Community Health Council, St. Anns Gardens, Manchester, 1982.

Political Issues in Nursing: Past, Present and Future, Volume 3
Edited by R. White

CHAPTER 8

Policy issues in continuing education for clinical nurses

JUDITH LATHLEAN, BSc (Econ), MA
*Formerly Research Fellow, Nursing Education Research Unit, King's College,
University of London, London, England*

Introduction

'Continuing education in nursing—luxury or necessity?' was the challenging title of a conference held at the King's Fund Centre, London, in 1984.[1] Indeed, in recent years, there has been an increasing number of initiatives focusing on the need for, and importance of, continuing education and various statements made by the statutory and professional nursing bodies in the United Kingdom, endorsing the view that further training, education and development after initial registration and qualification is a necessity rather than an 'optional extra'.

Continuing professional education has been defined by the American Nurses' Association as 'planned educational activities intended to build upon the educational and experiential bases of the professional nurse for the enhancement of practice, education, administration, or theory development to the end of improving the health of the public'.[2] In the United Kingdom, the term encompasses post-basic education, in-service training and staff development programmes. The distinction can be seen as one of national recognition. Thus, post-basic education includes courses for which a nationally recognized certificate *is* awarded whereas in-service training is described by the National Staff Committee for Nurses and Midwives as 'an aspect of the career-long development of nursing personnel, provided and controlled by the Employing Authority for which *no* nationally recognized certificate is awarded'.[3] Development programmes have a similar status.

This chapter considers the rationale for the increase of attention on continuing education, placing it in an historical context. Two particular innovations are highlighted which have arisen as a result of identified gaps in the training and preparation for the clinical roles of sister (head nurse) and staff nurse. Although the main thrust is the education, training and development of the qualified practitioner who works in a hospital setting much of the discussion is relevant to nurses practising in the community. Furthermore, basic training (that is, training for the initial qualification) and continuing professional education are inextricably linked: for example, changes or deficiencies in the former are bound to have implications for the latter; conversely the degree of continuing education experienced by trained staff affects their potential contribution to students. Some aspects of this will be touched upon.

The support for continuing education

It has commonly been asserted that continuing professional education is 'essential to the development of individual nurses' professional skills, to the efficiency of the health service and thus to developments in patient care'.[4] Reinforcing statements have been made by the statutory bodies responsible for nursing in the UK. For example, the United Kingdom Central Council for Nurses, Midwives and Health Visitors (UKCC) states in the Code of Professional Conduct:

Each registered nurse, midwife and health visitor is accountable for his or her own practice, and in the exercise of professional accountability shall . . .
3. take every reasonable opportunity to maintain and improve professional knowledge and competence
4. acknowledge any limitations of competence and refuse in such cases to accept delegated functions without first having received instruction in regard to those functions and having been assessed as competent.[5]

Clearly such a statement has potentially great implications for nursing practice and for continuing education. Further, the UKCC had denoted 1988 as the year during which the individual nurse, upon re-registration, will need to demonstrate that she has taken the opportunity to maintain and improve her own knowledge and skills. They are now referring to the end of the decade as the time when all nurses will have mandatory reorientation. Maud Storey (then Registrar and Chief Executive of UKCC) stressed that 'this does not simply refer to attendance at readily available courses, and the broad deployment of valuable resources. The individual nurse will need to take responsibility for her own development.'[6]

Such an approach had previously been advocated by the National Staff Committee in 1981:

> Every individual nurse of whatever grade or sphere of work should be aware of the need to update and expand her knowledge and skills. Fundamental in this is the commitment to assess critically her own learning needs and search and find appropriate resources and become self-directing in respect of her own learning.[3]

The National Boards for England, Wales and Scotland, too, have affirmed their positions in relation to continuing education.[7,8] Although to date only one (the National Board for Scotland) has actually issued guidelines[9] based on the recommendations of the report of the Working Party on Continuing Education for the Nursing Profession in Scotland,[10] clearly both the UKCC and the National Boards are deemed to have a responsibility 'in the context of their already adopted policies, to decide how to take forward the question of post registration education'.[11] In this respect, the UKCC's statement about the need is unequivocal: that there should be a coherent, comprehensive, cost-effective framework of education beyond registration. The detail of a suitable framework has yet to be debated and agreed.

The spotlight has certainly been on basic training recently.[7,11,12] But just as the Royal Commission on the National Health Service stated in 1979,[13] there appears to be agreement that basic education can only be a foundation, though one that ensures a life-long progression of professional learning.

The needs of qualified staff

The recognition of the need for further training is not new, particularly in relation to the preparation for, and the practice of, certain roles, notably those of the ward sister and nurse manager. The former has been the subject of specific attention for years. In the immediate post-war period, the Working Party on the Training and Recruitment of Nurses stated that:

> The particular problem of providing suitable 'post-graduate' prep-
> aration for ward sisters requires special consideration. . . . In
> comparison with facilities provided in some other countries, the
> opportunities in Great Britain . . . are at present very restricted.[14]

This concern, combined with the problems of trained staff wastage, prompted the Ministry of Health to ask the King Edward's Hospital Fund for London (King's Fund) to consider establishing courses which would prepare young trained nurses for work as ward sisters. As a result, a residential training centre for ward sisters was established in London in 1949.

It is interesting to note that, at the outset, the areas in which ward sisters were considered to need help bore a remarkable similarity to the needs of today: for example, they included the teaching of student nurses, personal relationships and 'modern' methods of staff manage-ment, and the efficient administration of the ward. The King's Fund continued with courses to develop such aspects into the 1960s, commenting in its Annual Report (1962) that 'it seems a matter of serious consideration whether the courses should not be regarded as an essential part of a ward sister's training rather than being available for a privileged few.'

This tension between training for the few—the specific development of an elite or the concentration on those with the greatest needs—and training for all, has been a recurring theme throughout post-basic education. The early provision made by the King's Fund Ward Sister College, alongside the three-month courses run by the Royal College of Nursing (RCN), plus a limited number of regional courses, exemplifies training which could only involve a very small proportion of nurses in that grade. However, in respect of the management role of the sister, the Salmon Report[15] and the National Nursing Staff Committee[16] sought to shift the emphasis and stimulate provision of places for all ward sisters on first-line management courses. Needless to say, with an esti-mated 33 000 sisters in 1968, and an annual requirement of 4300 places on courses, demand far outstripped supply. Furthermore, the feedback from sisters attending such courses was not always encouraging. For example, there was evidence that staff who attended the courses gener-ally enjoyed the experience but found difficulty in applying the knowl-edge gained to their jobs.[17,18,19] Later studies showed sisters to be critical of these courses. For example, Farnish found that some sisters, when asked to reflect on their preparation and training, described their experiences of courses using the terms 'conveyor belt' and 'sheep dip' approach. There was little apparent relationship between theory and practice (in the ward situation) and sisters were alienated by the emphasis on the academic and industry-orientated approach to management.[20]

Continuing education and the sister's role

Although the ward sister has been described since the time of Florence Nightingale as 'the head of the ward, responsible directly to the matron, . . . upon [whom] rests the management of the ward and direction of ward staff'[21] the role has received particular attention in the past decade. A number of research studies have served to reinforce the importance of the sister, for example as 'the only nurse who has direct managerial responsibilities for both patients and nurses'[22] and as the key person controlling the ward learning environment.[23,24] They have also suggested how the role can and should be developed, arguing that an important way in which sisters learn their job is by observing other more experienced sisters. This led to the recommendation that: 'Consideration be given to designated training wards for ward sisters in which the opportunity to work with role models and to learn to manage the nursing in its operational environment could be combined with theoretical work.'[25]

A training scheme for sisters

Despite the demise of the King's Fund courses for ward sisters in the late 1960s since 'it was felt that responsibility for such training might reasonably be accepted by professional and statutory bodies',[26] the King's Fund retained an interest in the development of the sister's role. Taking heed of current research, such as that of Pembrey,[22] the Fund agreed to support an experimental scheme for the training of ward sisters. The scheme was established in two London hospitals in 1979, and the results were evaluated by researchers from the Nursing Education Research Unit, Chelsea College, University of London.[27] (The evaluation research project was funded jointly by the Department of Health and Social Security (London) and by the King's Fund.)

This was seen as a unique opportunity to combine the development of standards of nursing care on particular wards which could then be used as 'training grounds' for other nurses (sisters and senior staff nurses) in the elements of their roles. The scheme was based on four premises:

(1) There is a need for *specific training* of ward sisters.
(2) This training should be *ward-based*.
(3) This requires a *joint* education/service approach.
(4) Nurses learn how to become ward sisters by *observing the behaviour* of other, more experienced ward sisters.

It was suggested that 'the best and quickest method for preparation (of ward sisters) is in the real life situation: where the nurse will encounter the day-to-day problems and challenges of running a ward, but will have the advantage of the support of a tutor to guide her studies and an experienced ward sister to act as a role model'.[28]

The approach of the scheme was very different from traditional management courses. Two wards were designated as 'training wards', each run by an experienced ward sister who was 'practised in the management of daily nursing on an individual basis, able to allocate work to the ward team and able to differentiate her role from that of the ward nurses'.[26] A nurse tutor organized the programme in each hospital and assisted with an understanding of the concepts and options available when issues of management, nursing care and teaching were discussed. The roles of training ward sister and nurse tutor were together known as the preceptors.[29]

The programme was of six months duration: the first twelve weeks constituted the formal course when the course members (trainees) were 'attached' to the training wards, and were supernumerary to normal ward staffing establishment. The trainee would then take up post as ward sister on another ward, with follow-up support for a further twelve weeks. This took the form of ward visits by a preceptor to assist the now practising ward sister in meeting her objectives and a small number of seminars/tutorials.

The aim of the programme was 'to prepare registered general nurses to function efficiently as ward sisters'.[30] Five aims in relation to specific knowledge, skill and behaviour were given—the management of patient care, teaching, ward management, personnel management and nursing research. The detailed knowledge required, and objectives to be achieved, were expressed within a curriculum plan.[30]

It was envisaged that learning would occur as a result of a number of different opportunities, notably working alongside and observing the sister of the training ward and critically discussing and analysing her performance, taking part in tutorials, seminars and lectures, undertaking a project and preparing written assignments and making internal and external visits.

The progress of the trainees and the effectiveness of the programme were assessed in a number of different ways, and the scheme was modified in line with feedback from the internal evaluation conducted in the main by the course tutors, and findings from the external evaluation project. This was facilitated by the use of an action research approach for the external evaluation which meant that the analysis of the scheme was conducted in a series of phases. Results from early phases were discussed with the schemes' promoters (the Kings Fund and selected staff from the two participating hospitals) and joint decisions were made about subsequent changes that would be implemented. The effects of these changes then became the subject of study in later phases of the research.[27]

Issues raised by the evaluation project

The aim of the King's Fund in setting up the experimental scheme, and in supporting its evaluation, was not to produce a blueprint for a scheme to train nurses for the sister's role but rather to develop guidelines for action. A number of *core themes* or elements emerged. These appeared to be fundamental to the success of the approach. Further, a set of *options* became apparent.

First, the evaluation supported the view expressed independently[20,31] that it is important to make a *specific* investment in training and support for the ward sister role. This appears necessary both in terms of the increased expectations of contemporary sisters and to enable a more efficient and motivated workforce. If sisters are successfully to fulfil the extended role of an autonomous clinical manager (as envisaged by the RCN) then 'this implies extensive clinical expertise and a preparation for clinical management in excess of present provisions for this grade'.[32]

There was evidence from the evaluation to suggest that the majority of those taking part in the scheme benefited in all aspects of their role. Increased knowledge and skill were identified by trainees themselves, preceptors and managers particularly with respect to interpersonal relationships, teaching (for some, not all), planning and implementing change. There was also an increase in confidence for most. Further, the course encouraged self-analysis, and reflection on career aspirations. This did not always result in a greater commitment to ward sistering (in one instance, a trainee was helped to reach the decision that she should leave nursing, in another that clinical teaching was more appropriate) but for the majority it developed awareness of the role and strengthened motivation.

There was also some indication that the beneficial effects of the scheme extended beyond the course members. For example, although not conclusive, there was a tendency for fewer learner shifts to be lost for sickness in wards managed by the 'King's Fund sisters' when compared with similar non-King's Fund sister wards. This is perhaps not surprising since it is known that one factor influencing learners' sickness and absence is their feeling of satisfaction about the ward and their relationship to the sister. Indeed, managers in one of the hospitals reported that many students indicated their enjoyment of working on the wards of former trainees 'since they found them good places to learn and the sisters were approachable'.[27]

Staff stability and low turnover on wards are factors which are often related to high levels of morale.[33] In this respect, managers commented on several incidences of wards where previous high turnover of staff and low morale were much improved when the ex-course members had been in post for several months. It appears, therefore, that participation in such a scheme can potentially affect organizational aspects in very positive ways—and ways that appeal to managers who are concerned with cost-effectiveness and the maximization of resources.

Second, there is little rationale for a scheme such as the one evaluated unless it is accepted that 'the ward sister critically influences the delivery of nursing and other services to the patient. The sister remains the key nurse in negotiating the care of the patient because she is the only person in the nursing structure who actually and symbolically represents continuity of care to the patient.'[22] The scheme attempted to promote this ethos. If the sister then found herself in an environment where such a role was not recognized or encouraged, participation in the programme could give rise to conflict and frustration. This reinforced the importance of involving nurses in the hierarchy in the planning and implementation of the scheme, plus close working with other members of the health-care team such as medical and paramedical staff in the clarification of mutual roles.

Third, there is a need to examine the sister role and the context within which it is located. Although the scheme is based on the notion that there are common principles and areas of responsibility across different sister posts, there are also variations such as those to be found between different specialties and in different geographical locations. Consider, for example, the work of the surgical ward sister which includes the organization of pre-operative preparation, the scheduling of nurses to accompany patients between ward and operating theatre, the administration of post-surgical therapies and monitoring. The emphasis is on speed in a busy ward atmosphere, since value is placed on 'getting patients up and out'. The sister in a geriatric ward may well have different priorities such as the achievement of rehabilitation rather than total recovery, the involvement of the relatives in the care of the patient, coping with the emotional problems of nursing dying patients, contending with the low status sometimes accorded to the care of the elderly which can affect the supply of resources[34] and the motivation of staff in a less favoured area of nursing.

Further, environmental factors can affect the role of the sister. For example, trained staff turnover tends to be higher in London than in the provinces: a relatively stable workforce can promote continuity of care but can also militate against beneficial change and the influx of new ideas. Also, the organizational structure can affect the role; for example, the absence or presence of clinical teachers on the wards, the balance of trained to untrained staff and the existence of other roles such as senior sisters. The suggestion is not that all sister roles should be treated as different and unique; rather that training be sufficiently flexible to allow the implications of alternative priorities to be examined—there may well need to be emphasis on certain skills in preference to others.

A fourth key element is the value of organizing training so as to maximize the learning that takes place from working with other more experienced sisters. There are various ways in which this can be achieved; the scheme afforded the opportunity to try out some of them. For example, initially trainees worked on the same shifts as the sister preceptor of the designated training wards for at least three-fifths of the time. They jointly undertook aspects of the role, such as the allocation of work and the management of patient care. However, and particularly as the number of trainees increased, this caused some stress, both for the sister preceptor and for the trainees themselves. Trainees found their role on the ward unclear. The sister found it difficult to cope with perhaps four or five supernumerary trainees most of whom had been appointed as sisters and were therefore at a similar level to herself. They needed a useful learning experience while on the ward— but they were not part of the ward team.

The situation was clarified in one of the hospitals by ensuring that the trainees were in an observation rather than in a working role with some discussion of the sister's performance, first only on the training ward and subsequently on a number of wards. Thus, trainees were able to see several ward sisters at work—both in different and similar areas to the ones they themselves would be working in. In the other hospital, trainees both observed on the training ward and worked with a sister on a ward of the kind that they would subsequently be running.

A fifth element of importance is the need of ward sisters, particularly when newly appointed, for support in their practice. (This has been very evident in a number of other studies also; for example those by Cortazzi and Roote,[35] Pembrey[22] and Runciman.[36]) The support may come from a number of sources such as peers, managers, education staff or an external agency. There appears to be merit in not only relying on the management structure to provide the support; there are some aspects of the sister's job which can be more appropriately shared with colleagues or with someone who is not part of the system by which the sister is judged. The scheme facilitated the establishment and continuation of arrangements which promoted mutual—and comfortable—discussion of ideas, problems and the revealing of weaknesses.

A theme that links all of these five fundamental elements is that of management commitment. 'If managers believe that the ward sister role is crucial in ensuring effective clinical management, and if they have a clear and realistic conception of this role, then they will be prepared to allocate resources for specific training.'[37]

The options that appear to be open to those considering this kind of approach relate to a number of questions. First, who should this training be for? There was considerable debate during the scheme: the majority supported the view of the scheme as most appropriate for sisters when newly appointed immediately prior to taking over their wards. The reasons included: the difficulty of really appreciating the role of the sister until the reality of the transition from staff nurse was experienced; absence from the ward was likely to be less disruptive if the sister had only just been appointed and the second part of the course was problematic if the nurse did not have her own ward to go to.

Set against this was the view that if the scheme was to be a *preparation* for the role, it should be directed at the senior staff nurse about to apply for promotion. Problems related to this included the fact that not all of the participants would then go on to sister posts in that particular authority. With district funding of the scheme, there was some reluctance to train nurses for posts, only to 'lose' them to another health authority. The consideration of 'where to start' and 'which grade of nurse should have the training and preparation' is also a feature of other educational innovations, including the one referred to in the latter part of the chapter.

Practically, if such a scheme were to be restricted to newly appointed ward sisters, it is likely that many districts would have a dearth of candidates at times. When the scheme was first mounted, the turnover of trained staff (sisters) was higher. Cases were known of nurses being appointed as sisters within six months of registration—an alarming thought when the responsibilities of the job are considered. This appears considerably less likely in the present climate, although there are a number of hospitals experiencing difficulty in recruiting—and retaining—well-trained and well-experienced nurses to fill certain posts at both staff nurse and sister level. The response of some health authorities who are running programmes for sisters (for example, the London Post-Graduate Teaching Hospitals[38]) is to widen the net to include a range of sisters from different specialties and units, and at different stages in their careers as sisters.

The second question is what should be the location? The scheme started as a resource for the district but was subsequently extended in one case to include sisters from elsewhere. This has the potential, however, to dilute the beneficial effects of the identification of the host hospital with the scheme. One of the advantages of such a scheme (which could be described as 'in-house' and 'ward-oriented') over certain alternatives is its role basis and close relationship to the institutional setting of the participants.

A third question is what should be the structure of the programme? In this respect 'there appears to be merit in a programme with two aspects—one concentrating on the more formal aspects of learning and the other on the application of this learning in a supportive clinical environment'.[39] However, there are apparently viable alternatives to a major 'theoretical' block, followed by a similar length period of semi-supervised or supported practice. For example, the programme could comprise a series of modules or study days interspersed with ward work. This has the advantage of decreasing the length of time a course member is away from her ward, but does entail frequent alternations of course and ward work which can be stressful for some.

It might also be possible to consider greater flexibility in programme structure to gain one that is more matched to the needs of individuals. (This is another theme which reoccurs in the evaluation of the staff nurses' scheme described later.) For example, if this kind of structure is retained, some nurses would seem to benefit from more support during the second part of the programme, whereas others are more confident and able to progress with less support. The support might be in the form of consultancy or (as is the case in the Oxfordshire Health Authority) by means of a 'contract' between nurse and facilitator.

Finally, what should be the theoretical input? The experience of the course confirmed the comprehensiveness of the curriculum, in that no additional subjects were suggested as appropriate for inclusion. The main criticism related to the perceived inadequate coverage of some of the topics rather than their omission from the plan. Obviously, curricula need to be brought in line with current preoccupations, and modified as the nature and expectations of the role change. Thus, for example, since this scheme was in operation, there has been much more emphasis on the role of the sister in relation to ward budgeting, cost-effectiveness, quality assurance, the part they should play in the development of their trained as well as learner nurses and the management of patient care in hitherto unknown areas such as the AIDS patient. There have been several major reports (referred to earlier) with the potential to change nursing, particularly basic education. These could have a marked affect on the role of the sister.

This chapter can only touch on a small number of the issues raised by the scheme and its evaluation. For further detail the interested reader is directed to the full report.[27] Since this evaluation, although DHSS and the statutory bodies have not actually issued a dictum that all newly appointed sisters should have preparation for their role, the need has certainly been highlighted and the frequency of articles in the press, about schemes for sisters, is an indication of the increased attention being paid by many health districts. Further, the plight of ward sisters and the importance of their training and education was reiterated in a major nursing conference in Harrogate (referred to as the Harrogate seminar) in 1981, although it was in fact the newly registered staff nurse who was singled out for special attention.

The holding of this seminar—entitled 'Professional Development in Clinical Nursing—the 1980s'—was an interesting new way of attempting to reach agreement between DHSS, the statutory and professional bodies and other groups and factions within nursing, about the best way forward in nursing in order to improve standards of care and enhanced career prospects.[40] It was in part stimulated by a report of a working group which looked at the promotion of careers in clinical nursing.[41]

As a result of discussion at the seminar, it was recommended by participants that

> newly registered nurses should have a period of professional consolidation and development following registration. This period would consist of supervised and supported practice in a designated training area and would take the form of a 'core professional

module'—applicable to nurses in any branch of nursing. A small number of experimental schemes are to be evaluated and for these a common framework will be required.[42]

Professional development schemes for newly registered nurses

Professional development schemes have the potential to address many issues in nursing, and a number of these were behind the establishment of the three experimental schemes, either explicitly or implicitly. The first major area is that of standards of care including problems related to the process of nursing, to structure and to outcome.

With respect to the former, through research studies, reports of working groups and the observations of professional organizations, concerns have been expressed about poor standards in physical care (such as infrequent turning of patients[43], inappropriate pre-operative starvation times[44] and inadequate preparation and administration of feeds for unconscious patients[45]); in psychological care (for example, inadequate counselling and explanation about treatments, limited verbal interaction with patients[46] and, within psychiatric hospitals, the provision of care which is 'custodial rather than therapeutic'[47]) and in the planning and organization of care (for example, failure to establish a 'continuous and dynamic pattern of assessment, planning, action and review'[48] on an individualized patient basis[22]).

Problems of structure have also been highlighted: those that could be affected by the scheme include staffing (such as the inequable distribution of nurses in the more attractive specialities at the expense of the 'Cinderella' ones of geriatrics and psychiatry), the imbalance of trained and untrained staff in some hospitals and wards, and the wastage of student and trained manpower; education, training and career opportunities—their relative dearth sometimes combined with lack of knowledge about them, or limited motivation for self-pursuit.

Although 'nursing has not yet developed to the point at which causal relationships may be established between nursing actions and improvement in patient problems',[49] it seems feasible to assume that inadequacies in the process and structure of nursing can affect the patient. For example, if nurses do not have certain skills and knowledge, it is unlikely that patients will receive the care they need and standards will be low.

A second area of concern which it was hoped the schemes might be able to tackle was the development and clarification of roles of trained nurses.

Although the schemes focused on the newly registered nurse, it was hoped that they would have beneficial effects for other grades and types of staff, particularly ward sisters who were to play a key role in facilitating the learning for the newly registered nurses on the scheme. There was concern about the fact that a registered nurse with no relevant additional academic or clinical experience can be appointed as a sister,[41] about sisters' lack of preparation and development[50] and about the lack of clarity over, and differentiation between their roles and those of other ward staff.[22,51]

Thirdly, the schemes were to be set up within existing resources, and it was envisaged that they would result in increased efficiency and reduced wastage such as 'decreased staff turnover costs, decreased short-term absence, retention of (expensively trained) qualified staff and greater control over resources by clinical leaders in addition to provision of a proper standard of care to patients by trained staff and improved morale of staff'.[40]

The aim of the schemes was 'to achieve professional consolidation and development where "professional development" was seen to include a number of aspects: clinical practice and the management of patient care, accountability and personal responsibility, self-awareness and direction, skills and responsibilities in relation to the nurse's own development, research awareness, and relationships and communication.'[52]

The framework (provided by DHSS) outlined the proposed structure of the schemes, including the programme, participants, training areas and staff. The core module was to be a six-month programme in two parts of thirteen weeks each. This was to be a period of supervised and supported practice on a ward, with sixteen study days, three in the first three months, thirteen in the second. Initially the schemes were to be for a selection of newly registered nurses for whom suitable, designated training areas were available. These areas were defined as 'any area providing appropriate experience and training—e.g. medical/surgical; mental handicap; community—headed by an experienced clinical leader (sister)'. She would have the main responsibility for the development and monitoring of the individual nurse. A tutor would be involved with the theoretical content of the course and a clinically experienced nurse should be available to the participants as a facilitator. Alternatively, one person could occupy both roles. Individuals' performance would be assessed and the scheme would be planned by a mixed group of education and service staff.

In order to judge the effectiveness of the schemes and the extent to which they addressed the concerns outlined above, an independent evaluation of three experimental schemes was set up with government funds. The project lasted for three years at the end of which a major report was produced;[51] this raised a large number of important issues, some of which are now discussed.

The outcomes of the evaluation

The evaluation of the post-registration development schemes focused on a number of different aspects such as the needs nurses tended to have when they had completed basic training and were embarking on their first staff nurse post; the opportunities that existed for development and support; the changes that occurred in nurses during their first six to ten months as qualified nurses (both those taking part in the scheme and those who were not) and the processes that appeared to promote or hinder developments. Although the data were collected from a relatively small number of nurses (just over 100 staff nurses took part in a questionnaire study and 12 were studied in considerable detail over a six-month period), the results were considered to be illustrative of the situation of staff nurses on a much wider basis.[53] Both those nurses who were participating in the schemes and those who were not were included in the evaluation.

The role and needs of the newly registered nurse

Although individual differences were apparent, overall, newly registered nurses were found to have needs for development and support in seven aspects: the knowledge and skills required for the clinical and management aspects of their role as staff nurses; interpersonal skills and knowledge, including communication with patients, relatives and other staff and teaching; autonomy, including the ability to make decisions and the capacity for self-direction and analytical thought; personal development such as awareness of own needs, strengths and weaknesses, confidence and motivation; attitudes in relation to current professional issues; career (commitment and planning) and the ability to cope with stress in their own role.

In addition, in practice it was found that the nurses often had considerable responsibilities in the 'technical' and interpersonal areas of their role—responsibilities that seemed to be beyond those of a nurse who has only just qualified and might be more fitting for a senior staff nurse or even a ward sister. For example, although the proportion of shifts that the nurse spent in charge of the ward varied, for the majority this was a regular experience. When in charge, the nurse was often involved in work allocation, drug rounds, doctors' rounds, liaison with other members of the health-care team and with relatives, and with clerical work. Mostly, the involvement with the patients was limited.

When not in charge, the most frequent role of the newly registered nurse was that of team leader, which often included not insubstantial amounts of 'paperwork', teaching sessions, liaison with other (non-nursing) staff, dealing with emotionally difficult tasks such as care of the dying patient and communicating with distressed and bereaved relatives, counselling and assessing students. This raises important considerations; for example, the feeling of many staff nurses that they lack preparation for their role, particularly in relation to management tasks and relationships with other staff. This was also a theme which emerged from an earlier research study by Vaughan[54] and it tends to support the view expressed by the UKCC that 'the system [of educational preparation] must be seen as . . . flawed'.[11] However, even with changes in basic education, there are some particular aspects which are likely to remain, such as the feeling and actuality of the increased responsibility, and the expectations that others have of a trained nurse as opposed to a learner, which are only experienced with the transition from student to registered nurse. Also, there are needs which can not be met by preparation prior to taking on a role such as those for support, for supervised practice and for feedback on performance and progress.

Second, the role of the newly registered nurse is often, in reality, very similar to that of more senior nurses, leading to high levels of responsibility and stress. In this respect, the evaluation report recommended that 'the role of a newly registered nurse should be more clearly defined and differentiated from that of the senior staff nurse and the ward sister. [Further, she] should not be put in full charge of the ward without support and supervision for several months, thus enabling a gradual path to the acceptance of complete responsibility.'[55]

Opportunities for development and support

Opportunities for the development and support of the inexperienced nurse can come in a number of ways such as contact with the ward sister during ward work; formal meetings and discussions with the sister; contact with other ward nurses, service managers, staff in other disciplines, education staff and peers; study days; working with a list of aims and objectives; structured assessment; projects; private study; event diary and educational visits.

In the evaluation project, the opportunities for nurses participating in the scheme (course members) and those not on the scheme (non-course members) were compared. On average, course members fared better in that they had more—and better quality—opportunities than did non-course members. However, this was not always the case. For example, on average, the number of shifts that course members and their sister were on together varied between 15 and 20 in the first six months post-registration, whereas, on average, non-course members worked the same shifts as their sister for 20 to 25 days in the same period. This difference appeared to be due to course members' attendance at more study days than non-course members. Even when nurses worked the same shift as the sister they would not necessarily have much contact. In over half the cases, the nurse and/or her sister stated how little they saw of each other: in general, if they were on the same shift they would be occupied with different aspects of the work.

Although the individual differences were pronounced, on the whole opportunities for course members were significantly greater than for non-course members in relation to their individual contact with education staff, contact with peer group, study days, provision of a list of aims and objectives and a structure for assessment, projects, private study (reading) and event diary.

Developments and processes in individual nurses

Developments were found to occur in aspects of all areas of the nurse's role, namely: technical knowledge and skills, interpersonal skills, autonomy, personal development, attitudes towards nursing and career aspirations. However, the extent of the development varied considerably between individuals, although overall it was greater in course members than non-course members. Examples of where positive change was particularly identified in course members include a greater awareness of the patient as a whole, increased understanding of the role of the registered nurse, improvement in the use of non-verbal communication, greater confidence in the ability to teach and support junior staff, improvement in organization when running a shift, maintenance and possibly heightening of responsibility and motivation related to their own development and a better understanding of nursing philosophy and issues.

At the end of the evaluation period (that is, when the nurses involved in the study had been registered for between six and ten months) although some room for improvement remained with all of the staff nurses, this was nowhere near as marked or as extensive with the majority of the course members as it was with those who had not taken part in the scheme. In addition, there was even evidence of some deterioration for a few individuals in certain aspects, for example in the nurse's ability to cope with stress, make decisions and in the degree of soundly-based confidence. Actual deterioration was, however, found to be more common amongst non-course members.

The ways in which developments appear to be promoted were examined. These can be divided into three groups: *general processes* which include learning from experience, role-modelling and individualized learning; *independent learning*, including skills practice (with feedback), individual study and projects, and educational visits; and *facilitation*— discussion of experience, feedback on abilities and progress, comparison with peers, provision of alternatives and additional information in relation to own methods, justification of own views and discussion of feelings.

Without exception among the study nurses, experience was considered to be of great importance in promoting their development. It is important, however, to distinguish between experience *per se* (that which happened merely as a result of working as a registered nurse regardless of the environment) and experience with specific conditions or features. It was evident that it was the latter that was most beneficial. The features included:

recognition by self and others of the learning status of the nurse, watching others, asking questions, availability of support and advice from other staff, teaching and guidance, gradual increase in responsibility, and, importantly, 'getting it right' or 'coping'. The nurses who showed the most signs of development had certain other opportunities, away from the work situation, which enhanced their learning from experience such as the opportunity to reflect on their work, to receive feedback and to compare their progress and problems with others. On the other hand, nurses who developed little . . . were those for whom factors other than experience *per se* were less apparent, or who seemed unable to take advantage of them if they were available.[56]

A similar consideration appears to pertain with learning by role-modelling. The effectiveness of learning in this way seems to be related to three factors: the quality of the role model, the nurse's opportunity to explore alternatives and the initial qualities of the individual learner. Although the ward sisters saw themselves to some extent as role models, particularly in view of the two points raised earlier—the tendency for the nurse only to spend a small number of shifts working with the sister, and the lack of differentiation between the roles of registered nurses—dependance on this way of learning may be somewhat inappropriate.

To some extent, learning needs were met by the provision believed to be relevant for all newly registered nurses. However, some conscious assessment of individual need was found, and this was more effective when it was structured and involved the nurse in conjunction with a senior or tutor. The consideration of individual needs and interests seemed to stimulate involvement of nurses in their own learning—somehow it felt more relevant to them, more in line with what they needed to know and do.

Although in theory all nurses have the opportunity to experience the general processes and, to a certain extent, the independent learning processes described above, few of the non-course members were able to benefit from those referred to as 'facilitation'. For example, it was much easier to identify a staff member who could be described as a facilitator for the course members, and structured peer group contact—much valued by course members—was rare amongst the other group. Indeed, 'those [processes] called "facilitation" appeared crucial since they could initiate, guide and enhance many of the other processes and also help integration of learning from different sources'.[57]

The way forward

The findings of the evaluation project indicate that there is a need for a comprehensive plan for staff development which takes into account that all trained staff require continuing education and support. UKCC's Project 2000 suggests that the framework for this should include 'opportunities to consolidate learning in the post-registration period [and] opportunities for updating knowledge and skills, bearing in mind the observation that professional knowledge is now out of date in as little as five to eight years'.[58] And 'although professional courses should obviously be part of this, if provision is to be made which is sufficiently flexible, likely to meet both organisational and individual needs, and feasible in terms of resources, this may mean a move away from traditional courses, some of which are costly to run and inadequately related to ward work'.[59] Organizational needs include the promotion of high standards of care, the retention of highly skilled, well-motivated nurses in clinical settings and the attraction of nurses to less popular areas of nursing such as care of the elderly and psychiatry.

Conclusion

Certain common themes and issues emerge from both of the studies described and from other related literature. To conclude, a few of these threads are now drawn out. First, there is the issue of selectivity. Both of the programmes (the ward sister and the professional development schemes) involved only a proportion of the ward sisters and staff nurses in the host authorities (although the original plan for the newly registered nurses' scheme was for the eventual inclusion of all newly registered nurses) and even within these groups there was discussion about who should be selected—the most able (who could then go on to lead and develop others), those in the greatest 'need' (however this was defined), or a mixture of the two?

At present, very few health authorities have well-developed programmes, such as the schemes described, for their trained staff but many offer National Board courses in post-basic clinical nursing studies of various kinds. However, Rogers conducted a study which revealed that, at the most, only 9.7 per cent of all qualified nurses employed by the NHS possessed a post-basic qualification, and not all of those were still in nursing.[60] In a second study, Rogers found that respondents were evenly split between those who considered continuing education opportunities to be adequate and those who did not.[4] Here there was a distinction between the feelings of enrolled nurses, who in general felt excluded, staff nurses who considered that opportunities tended to go in preference to ward sisters who, in turn, felt constrained by time and lack of places on courses and study days.

One of the problems appears to be the narrow conception that many nurses have of continuing education: the majority appear to equate the term with courses, study days or programmes. If continuing education opportunities are interpreted more widely—to include a whole range of provision such as the opportunity to work alongside more experienced nurses; supported and supervised practice; peer groups and ward forums; discussion of performance, assessment (including self-assessment) and feedback; the opportunity for private study and use of distance learning packages as well as course and study days—it is more likely that the plea for continuing education for all trained nurses will become a reality.

These studies highlight the importance of considering the organization as well as the individual. This is relevant in a number of different ways. For example, it appears that initiatives directed primarily towards the individual can promote organizational aims such as the retention of trained and motivated nurses in nursing at a time of particular concern over shortage of manpower. Second, it is a waste of resources if individuals are trained and developed in isolation, only to return to an environment which does not facilitate the use of the benefits gained. It is well known that individuals and organizations are resistant to change: conversely, there are strategies for achieving change such as those which utilize the power of the group rather than relying on the individual.

It has been argued that hitherto the British nursing profession has held quite strong anti-education attitudes which contrast quite sharply with the North American situation where 'nurses demonstrate considerable commitment to a great variety of continuing education'.[61] However, with the current impetus from the UKCC, the National Boards and DHSS, the discussions about mandatory education and criteria for relicensing, and the more general recognition that continuing education has an important part to play in the development of nursing as a profession, it is likely that a shift in attitudes will be apparent. Only then is this likely to be matched by a shift in the allocation of resources.

References

1. King's Fund Centre, *Continuing Education in Nursing—Luxury or Necessity*. Report of a conference, King Edward's Hospital Fund for London, November 1984.
2. American Nurses' Association, *Standards for Continuing Education in Nursing*. American Nurses' Association, Missouri, 1984.
3. Department of Health and Social Security, *Recommendations on the Organisation and Provision of Continuing In-Service Education*. Report of the National Staff Committee for Nurses and Midwives, DHSS, 1981.
4. Rogers, J., *Continuing Professional Education for Qualified Nurses*. Background paper for King's Fund Centre conference entitled 'Continuing Professional Education for Nurses: Signposts from Research', King's Fund, London, October 1986.
5. United Kingdom Central Council, *Code of Professional Conduct for the Nurse, Midwife and Health Visitor*, 2nd edition. UKCC, London, 1984.
6. Storey, Maud, 'Towards the year 2000', *Professional Nurse*, 1986, 1 (May), 204–206.
7. The English National Board for Nursing, Midwifery and Health Visiting,

Professional Education/Training Courses: Consultation Paper. ENB, London, 1985.

8. The Welsh National Board for Nursing, Midwifery and Health Visiting, *Strategy for Nursing in Wales.* WNB, Cardiff, 1987.

9. National Board for Nursing, Midwifery and Health Visiting for Scotland, *Guidelines for Continuing Education: Professional Studies 1 and 2.* NBS, Edinburgh, 1985.

10. National Board for Nursing, Midwifery and Health Visiting for Scotland, *Continuing Education for the Nursing Profession in Scotland.* NBS, Edinburgh, 1981.

11. United Kingdom Central Council, *Project 2000.* UKCC, London, 1986.

12. Royal College of Nursing, Commission on Nursing Education, *The Education of Nurses: a New Dispensation* (Judge Report). RCN, London, 1985.

13. Department of Health and Social Security, *Royal Commission on the National Health Service Report.* HMSO (Cmnd 7615), London, 1979.

14. Ministry of Health, Department of Health for Scotland, Ministry of Labour and National Service, *Report of the Working Party on the Recruitment and Training of Nurses* (Wood Report). HMSO, London, 1947.

15. Ministry of Health and Scottish Home and Health Department, *Report of the Committee on Senior Nursing Staff Structure* (Salmon Report). HMSO, London, 1966.

16. Department of Health and Social Security, *Management Development of Senior Nursing Staff in the Hospital Service.* Report of the National Staff Committee, DHSS, 1968.

17. Geddes, J., *An Evaluation of Ten First-Line Management Courses: Academic Year 1969–1970.* Unpublished Report, Leeds Health Authority, 1971.

18. Schurr, M. C., 'Learning together – 1', *Nursing Times*, 1973, **69** (22 November), 1582–1584.

19. White, D., 'Learning together – 2', *Nursing Times*, 1973, **69** (29 November), 1623–1625.

20. Farnish, S., *Ward Sister Preparation: a Survey in Three Districts.* Nursing Education Research Unit, Chelsea College, University of London, 1983.

21. Cope, Z., *A Hundred Years of Nursing at St. Mary's Hospital, Paddington.* Heinemann, London, 1955.

22. Pembrey, S. E. M., *The Ward Sister—Key to Nursing.* RCN, London, 1980.

23. Fretwell, J. E., *Ward Teaching and Learning.* RCN, London, 1982.

24. Orton, H. D., 'Ward learning climate and student nurse response', *Nursing Times*, Occasional Paper, 1981, **77**, No. 17.

25. See reference 22, p. 87.

26. Allen, H. O. A. (ed.), *The Ward Sister: Role and Preparation.* Baillière Tindall, Eastbourne, 1982.

27. Lathlean, J. and Farnish, S., *The Ward Sister Training Project.* Nursing Education Research Unit, Chelsea College, University of London, 1984.

28. Davies, C., 'Training for ward sisters: an innovative research and development project', *Nurse Education Today*, 1981, **1**, No. 2, 16–18.

29. The term 'preceptor' denotes a nurse who has the ability to integrate education and work values so that realistic strategies for resolving conflict

might be developed. Such a relationship allows the trainee to work and identify with a competent role model. This involves not only observation by the trainee but a planned two-way exchange of approaches and evaluation (after Kramer, M. and Schmalenberg, C., *Path to Biculturalism*, Wakefield (Mass.) Nursing Resources, 1977).

30. King Edward's Hospital Fund for London, *Ward Sister Preparation: a Contribution to Curriculum Building*. Project Paper Number 36, King's Fund, London, 1982.
31. Royal College of Nursing, *Towards a New Professional Structure for Nursing*. RCN, London, 1983.
32. See reference 31, p. 6.
33. Redfern, S., *Hospital Sisters*. RCN, London, 1981.
34. Baker, D., *Attitudes of Nurses to Care of the Elderly in Hospital*, PhD thesis, University of Manchester, 1978.
35. Cortazzi, D. and Roote, S., *Illuminative Incident Analysis*. McGraw-Hill, London, 1975.
36. Runciman, P., *Ward Sister at Work*. Churchill Livingstone, Edinburgh, 1983.
37. See reference 27, p. 125.
38. Dodwell, M., *London Post Graduate Teaching Hospitals Ward Sisters' Training Project: The Report*. LPTH, London, 1984.
39. See reference 27, p. 127.
40. Department of Health and Social Security, *Professional Development in Clinical Nursing—the 1980s*. DHSS, 1982.
41. Department of Health and Social Security, *Careers in Clinical Nursing*. DHSS, 1980.
42. See reference 40, p. 13.
43. Norton, D., McClaren, R. and Exton-Smith, A., *An Investigation of Geriatric Nursing Problems in Hospitals*. Churchill Livingstone, Edinburgh, 1975.
44. Hamilton-Smith, S., *Nil by Mouth*. RCN, London, 1972.
45. Jones, D. C., *Food for Thought*. RCN, London, 1975.
46. Macleod-Clark, J., 'Nurse–patient communication—an analysis of conversations from surgical wards'. In Wilson Barnett, J. (ed.), *Nursing Research—10 Studies in Patient Care*. John Wiley, Chichester, 1983.
47. Royal College of Nursing, *The State of Nursing: the RCN Submission to the Secretary of State for Social Services*. RCN, London, 1974.
48. Royal College of Nursing, *Standards of Nursing Care*. RCN, London, 1980.
49. See reference 48, p. 14.
50. Farnish, S., 'How are sisters prepared?' *Nursing Times*, Occasional Paper, 1985, **81**, No. 32.
51. Lathlean, J., Smith, G. and Bradley, S., *Post-Registration Development Schemes Evaluation*. Nursing Education Research Unit, King's College, University of London, 1986.
52. See reference 51, p. 10.
53. The usefulness and validity of the small-scale in-depth case-study approach for the evaluation and understanding of social settings is well supported by Walker, R., 'The use of case studies in applied research and evaluation'. In Hartnett, A. (ed.), *The Social Sciences in Educational Studies*. Heinemann, London, 1982.

54. Vaughan, Barbara, *The Newly Qualified Staff Nurse: Factors Affecting Transition.* MSc thesis, University of Manchester, 1980.
55. See reference 51, p. 87.
56. See reference 51, p. 59.
57. See reference 51, p. 67.
58. See reference 11, p. 51.
59. See reference 51, p. 86.
60. Rogers, J., *The Follow Up Study: Career Patterns of Nurses who Completed a Joint Board of Clinical Nursing Studies Certificate Course.* Report to the DHSS, DHSS, 1982.
61. Lahiff, Maureen, 'A step further'. In King's Fund Centre, *Continuing Education in Nursing—Luxury or Necessity.* Report of a conference, King Edward's Hospital Fund for London, November 1984.

Political Issues in Nursing: Past, Present and Future, Volume 3
Edited by R. White

CHAPTER 9

The development of nursing in South Africa

ROSALIE THOMPSON BSocSc (Nursing), RN, RM, DNE, MPubAdm
Professor and Head, Department of Nursing, University of Cape Town, South Africa

Introduction

> To look forward with vision, it is wise to glance backward with perception—not to be bound by history; nor to blame ourselves or our predecessors, but to learn lessons as a springboard to the future.[1]

Writing for a multi-national readership at this time in our history I find both daunting and challenging. No nurse, or indeed historian, could approach this subject without stating their major debt to Professor Charlotte Searle for her excellent treatise on the 'History of the Development of Nursing in South Africa 1652 to 1960' for which she received a DPhil Cum Laude in 1965 and, at the outset, I would like to acknowledge her and pay tribute to her leadership of the profession over the past half-century.

In order to provide a framework for the subsequent discussion on the development of professional nursing an overview of the country is given. The area of South Africa (SA) is about equal to the combined areas of West Germany, France, Italy, the Netherlands and Belgium and the distance from Cape Town to Pretoria is approximately equal to that between Amsterdam and Rome. South Africa consists of four Provinces—the Cape, the Orange Free State, Natal and the Transvaal. The map (Figure 1) indicates these together with the four Independent

RSA Total 27 722 100**

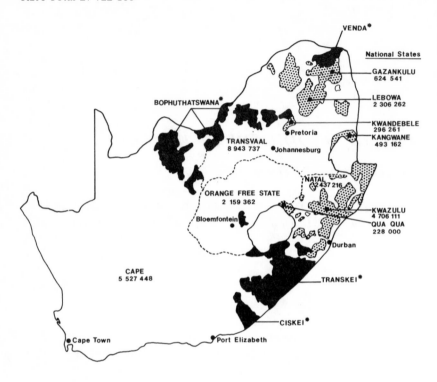

Source. Department of National Health and Population Development 1987
'The 1985 Census'. *Epidemiological Comments*, vol. 14, No. 1, pp. 19, 36.
Note
*These are the Independent States whose estimated population in 1985 is
5 550 000.
**Excluding the population of the Independent States.

Figure 1. The geographic distribution of the population, Republic of South
Africa, 1985

National States (Transkei, Bophuthatswana, Venda, Ciskei) and the
Self-Governing (National) States. The total population in 1980 was
estimated at 28 654 000 (self-governing and independent national states
included) and the percentage representation of the four main population groups was 72.2 per cent Black, 15.8 per cent Whites, 9.1 per
cent Coloureds and 2.9 per cent Asians.[2]

The complexity of the population is far greater than the official classification indicates—each of these major population groups can be divided into a number of subgroups with widely diversified cultural, ethnic, religious, language and constitutional differences. There are four distinct linguistic groups amongst the Blacks, and more than 50 per cent of the total Black population falls into one of these groups. The major groups represent approximately nine indigenous languages.[3] About 60 per cent of the White population as well as the majority of the Coloured people speak Afrikaans, whereas English is the mother tongue for just under 40 per cent of the White population and of a substantial number of the Asian population and of small numbers of the other population groups—the two official languages in the Republic of South Africa are English and Afrikaans.[4]

In the past only a few privileged Africans (Blacks) were sufficiently educated to become ministers of religion, doctors, nurses, teachers, lawyers or clerks and these people formed the Black elite and were afforded great prestige in their communities. However, this has changed with the emergence of a skilled and educated Black industrial working class.[5]

Not only have the Blacks acquired industrial skills but their academic skills are increasing too, as Table 1 indicates.

Table 1 University and/or college education received by the different population groups

	1970		1976		1985	
	No.	Percentage of population	No.	Percentage of population	No.	Percentage of population
Asians	3 474	0.7	7 176	1.1	17 300	2.01
Blacks	4 509	0.03	10 916	0.1	42 872	0.23
Coloureds	1 813	0.2	4 662	0.4	12 914	0.45
White	73 001	2.2	100 812	2.6	138 670	2.8
Total	82 797		123 566		211 756	

Sources
1. Van Rensburg, H. C. J. and Mans, A., *Profile of Disease and Health Care in South Africa*. Academia, Pretoria, 1982, p. 32.
2. South Africa, *South African Statistics*. Central Statistical Services, Pretoria, 1986, p. 1.5.
3. Department of National Health and Population Development, 'The 1985 Census', *Epidemiological Comments*, 1987, **14**, No. 1, 11.

A quiet revolution has begun in South Africa's universities.

Although each of them is either predominantly black or predominantly white, none of them is exclusively black or exclusively white. In every case all population groups are represented at each of the universities and all the evidence which we have suggests that this trend will continue and even increase.[6]

In South Africa Whites are mostly found in the upper socio-economic categories while the Blacks and Coloureds are mostly in the lower socio-economic groups. The Asians form an intermediate group.

The unique factor in the South African situation during the last 20 odd years has been the emergence, steady growth and coming to maturity of the African (Black) industrial working class and its entrance into politics. The apparatus, ideas and culture surrounding the socialization process of people in the African community are increasingly the same as those surrounding the socialization process of the White community. What you find in an African home is increasingly becoming the same as what you find in the White home.[7]

Occupation as such, but particularly as a facet of a person's general socio-economic status, undoubtedly plays an important role in regard to disease and health in populations and population groups. The South African labour market is to a large extent influenced by the country's multi-racial composition. The growth rate of the population during the period 1904–80 shows an average percentage increase per annum of 2.28. The Asian population (2.54 per cent) had the highest growth rate, followed by the Blacks and Coloureds (2.37 and 2.36 per cent respectively), and the Whites (1.86 per cent) have the lowest growth rate. This rate of increase is cause for concern as the economy cannot sustain this level.[8]

The rate of urbanization has also increased. In 1980 91.3 per cent of Asians, 77.4 per cent of Coloureds, 88.7 per cent of Whites and 38 per cent of Blacks were urbanized. It is estimated that by the year 2000 approximately 20 million Blacks will be living in urban areas which means a growth in the urban Black population from 37 per cent in 1980 to approximately 75 per cent.[9] This trend towards urbanization has important implications in the demand for, and the provision of, health services. Urban communities are easily brought within reach of organized health services whereas remote rural populations present significant problems. Adequate health care is hampered by natural barriers, poor roads, inadequate transport services ,and, as populations are often sparse, the doctor/population ratio is not economically viable. The effect of this on the practice of nurses in particular, as well as other health-care professionals, is significant.

The pyramid in Figure 2 represents an age-structure analysis and reveals the characteristics of a developing country with a large percentage of the population under 14 years of age (Asians 37 per cent, Blacks 41 per cent, Coloureds 39 per cent and Whites 28 per cent) and on the other hand the characteristics of a developed country with a large group over 65 years of age.[10] A high birth rate and a predominantly young population will remain the norm for decades to come and will impose great and growing demands on the provision of health-care services.[11] Of the population over the age of 65, 15 per cent, often with chronic illness or disability, have a greater need for health care than any other group.[12]

The characteristic profile of disease and mortality in South Africa is directly related to the distinctive socio-economic stratification—among Whites and Asians there is a chronic degenerative pattern with coronary heart disease, cancer of the stomach and prostate, duodenal ulcers and similar diseases of an affluent society as the main causes of disease and death. In contrast, the Blacks and Coloureds at the lower end of the socio-economic scale present a typical profile of infective disease and mortality in which infective and nutritional diseases such as tuberculosis, pneumonia, bronchitis, syphilis, kwashiorkor and rheumatic heart disease are predominant—thus their profile of morbidity and death is still dominated by typical 'social diseases'.[13] However, the incidence of hypertension and ischaemic heart disease is increasing amongst the urban Blacks with their growing affluence. With improving conditions there is an exchange of the diseases of poverty for the diseases of affluence. Both need to be attended to in any health-care system.

The nature of the health services in a country is affected not only by the size of the population but by the availability of the health-care personnel. The quality and numerical strength of these personnel are in turn determined by the quality and range of education and training facilities.

Nurses form the largest health service profession and their geographic distribution is also far more favourable than that of any other category of health care professional. Because of the maldistribution of other health care professionals (and workers) and the absolute manpower shortages in certain categories, more

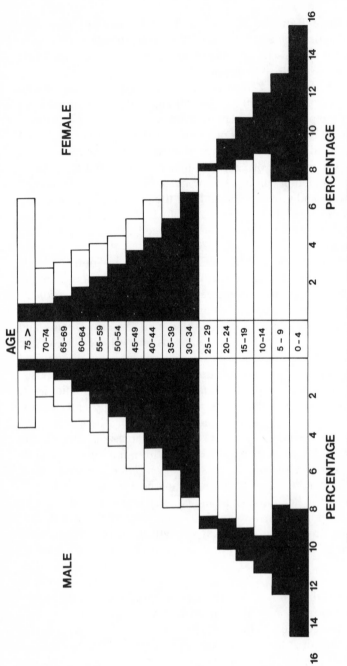

Figure 2. Population pyramid for South Africa 1985* ☐ White ■ 'Blacks'**
The White and 'Black' population pyramids from the 1985 census superimposed

Source. Department of National Health and Population Development 1987 'The 1985 Census'. *Epidemiological Comments*, vol. 14, No. 1, pp. 12–14.

Note

*Excluding the population of the Independent States (Transkei; Bophuthatswana; Venda and Ciskei]

**'Black' here includes Asian, Black and Coloured people.

is expected from nurses, who thanks to their more favourable distribution are in a position to fill in the shortages in addition to meeting the demands of their own profession.[14]

Table 2   Registered health professionals[a] (as at 1 January 1984) and ratio to population

Category	Ratio to population 1984	Total		% of total
Medical practitioners (including 1009 Interns)	1 : 1 490	19 118		
Medical students	1 : 5 825	4 893	24 011	12.52
Dentists	1 : 9 286	3 069		
Dental students	1 : 27 014	1 955	4 124	2.15
Pharmacists	1 : 4 376	6 513	6 513	3.40
Registered nurses	1 : 468	60 941		
Enrolled nurses	1 : 1 426	19 986		
Enrolled nursing assistants	1 : 759	37 571		
Student nurses	1 : 1 762	16 179		
Pupil nurses	1 : 5 931	4 805		
Pupil nursing assistants	1 : 7 000	4 071	139 567[c]	72.78
Supplementary health services personnel[b]	1 : 1 624	17 552	17 552	9.15
Total			191 767	100

Sources
1. SA Nursing Council, Circular 252/584, 1984.
2. de Villiers, J. C. (Chairman), Report and recommendations of the Committee of Enquiry on possible future facilities for medical and dental training, 1984.

Note
[a]Excluding chiropractors, homeopaths, herbalists and naturopaths.
[b]The supplementary health service personnel are:

Dieticians	259
Medical technologists (all categories)	2478
Clinical technologists	111
Psychologists	1495
Dental therapists	82
Oral hygienists	376
Occupational therapists	999
Optometrists	810
Physiotherapists	2364
Diagnostic radiographers	2518
Speech therapists & audiologists	704

cThis figure (139 567) represents the number of *persons* taking into account dual registrations and enrolments. The total number of registrations and enrolments (not persons) totals 143 559.
An enrolled nurse has successfully completed a 2-year course (post-10-years schooling) including an SA Nursing Council final examination.
A pupil nurse is a trainee enrolled nurse.
An enrolled nursing assistant has successfully completed an in-service training programme.
A pupil nursing assistant is a trainee enrolled nursing assistant.

A brief statistical overview of the health-care profession indicates that the current ratio of registered nurses and midwives to population is 1:435 if the population of the Independent States is excluded (and 1:522 including the population of the Independent States), whereas the ratio of registered medical practitioners and interns (in 1983) to population is 1:1490. The World Health Organization considers a ratio of 1 registered nurse to 500 of population as necessary in order to deliver a basic comprehensive health service in a Third World Country.[15]

Although the ratio of practising registered nurses to population is not quite as good, there is nonetheless a very high percentage of nurses practising. Registered nurses represent 42.2 per cent of all nurses as at 31 December 1986. Student nurses represent 9.3 per cent and the remaining 48.5 per cent consist of the subprofessional categories.[16]

When one considers a breakdown according to racial categories we find the situation as regards registered nurses not as optimal as it initially appears. While it appears that it will be possible to maintain existing registered nurse to population ratios amongst the Asiatic, Coloured and White population groups if the present growth rates are maintained, the number of Black nurses admitted to the profession needs almost to double if a ratio of 1 registered nurse to every 500 of population is to be attained by the year 2000. This is no mean challenge.[17] The shortage of teaching posts and the shortage of teaching staff remain the greatest stumbling blocks in the training programmes for Black nurses. Both these defects are due to economic factors, and are cause for concern.[18]
The small number of nursing trainees in all population groups is also disquieting. In the findings of a recent Committee of Enquiry appointed by the Minister of Health it was stated that

The greatest immediate need in South Africa, so far as health manpower is concerned, is for nurses—the State and the Nursing

Table 3 Ratio of qualified persons on the registers of the SA Nursing Council to the population: 1960–85

Year	RSA population				Percentage increase/decrease of qualified persons on registers of SANC	No. of qualified persons on the registers of the SA Nursing Council[a]				Ratio of qualified persons on the registers of the SA Nursing Council to population			
	White	Coloured & Asian	Black	Total		White	Coloured & Asian	Black	Total	White	Coloured & Asian	Black	Total
1960	3 088 492	1 986 383	10 927 922	16 002 797		17 947 (23.22%)	1 002 (68.16%)	5 147 (67.55%)	24 096	1:172	1:1982	1:2123	1:664
					1960–65								
1965	3 398 000	2 284 000	12 186 000	17 868 000		22 115 (12.18%)	1 685 (59.17%)	8 624 (40.57%)	32 424	1:154	1:1356	1:1413	1:551
					1965–70								
1970	3 021 040	2 723 310	15 427 880	21 446 169		24 808 (1.17%)	2 682 (32.74%)	12 123 (34.38%)	39 613	1:122	1:1015	1:1273	1:541
					1970–75								
1975	4 236 810	3 103 210	17 703 300	25 043 320		25 099 (8.61%)	3 560 (23.12%)	16 291 (19.56%)	44 950	1:169	1:872	1:1087	1:557
					1975–80								
1980	4 684 650	3 550 120	20 364 750	28 599 520		27 260[b] (12.20%)	4 383[b] (54.60%)	19 477[b] (35.60%)	51 120[b]	1:172	1:810	1:1046	1:559
					1980–85								
1985	4 947 100	3 723 500	19 951 500[c]	27 722 100		30 586	6 775	26 411	63 772	1:157	1:550	1:721	1:435

Sources
1. South African Bureau of Statistics, *Population census*. The Government Printer, Pretoria, 1960, pp. 2–3.
2. South African Nursing Association, The Board, *Report on nursing service in the Republic of South Africa*. SANA, Pretoria, 1966. p. 4.
3. South African Nursing Association, The Board, *Report on nursing service in the Republic of South Africa and the territory of South West Africa*. SANA, Pretoria, 1972, p. 10.
4. South African Nursing Association, The Board, *Report on nursing service in the Republic of South Africa, and the self-governing territories*. SANA, Pretoria, 1978, p. 2.
5. South Africa. Department of Statistics, *Population projections for the Republic of South Africa, 1970–2020*. The Government Printer, Pretoria, 1970, Report No. 02-06-01.
6. South African Nursing Council, *Report of the Sixth Council 1970–1975*. SANC, Pretoria, 1975, Annexure E, p. 6.
7. Department of National Health & Population Development, 'The 1985 Census', *Epidemiological Comments*, 1987, **14**, No. 1, 11 & 38.

Notes
[a]Not all persons registered are practising.
[b]1978 statistics.
[c]Excluding Independent States (±5 550 000 people mainly Black).

Table 4 Number of qualified persons (registered) on the registers of the SA Nursing Council and number practising 1960–86

| Year | White | Coloured (C) & Asian (A) | Black | Number practising (percentage in brackets) | | |
				White	Coloured and Indian	Black
1960	17 947	1 002	5 147			
1965	22 115	1 685	8 624			
1967	23 415	2 016	9 835			
1969	24 504	2 455	11 244	14 704 (60%)	2 097 (85.4%)	9 171 (81.6%)
1970	24 808	2 682	12 123			
1971	25 546	2 925	13 119	15 081 (59.03%)	2 337 (78.95%)	10 358 (78.95%)
1974	24 365	3 506	15 650	17 263 (70.85%)	3 051 (87%)	12 825 (82%)
1975	25 099	3 560	16 291			
1976	26 458	3 907	17 162	18 818 (71.12%)	3 404 (87.1%)	14 885 (86.7%)
1977	27 068	4 147	18 362			
1978	27 260	4 383	19 477			
1980	28 630	A. 931 / C. 4 143	21 318			
1982	30 667	A. 1 093 / C. 4 757	21 185			
1984	30 544	A. 1 228 / C. 5 242	25 331			
1985	30 825	A. 1 386 / C. 5 737	26 969	27 433 (89%)	A. 1 343 (97%) / C. 5 368 (94%)	18 557 (68.8%)[a]

Sources
1. South African Nursing Association, The Board, Report on nursing service in the Republic of South Africa. SANA, Pretoria, 1966.
2. South African Nursing Association, The Board, Report on nursing service in the Republic of South Africa and the territory. SANA, Pretoria, 1968, p. 3.
3. South African Nursing Association, The Board, Report on nursing service in the Republic of South Africa and the territory of South West Africa. SANA, Pretoria, 1972, p. 10.
4. South African Nursing Association, The Board, Report on nursing service in the Republic of South Africa. SANA, Pretoria, 1978.
5. South African Nursing Council, Circular C2/M79 (b) p. 6.
6. South African Nursing Council, Report of the Sixth Council. 1970–1975. SANA, Pretoria, 1975, Annexure E, p. 6.
7. South African Nursing Association, The Board, Report on nursing service and nursing education in the Republic of South Africa 1978–1983. SANA, Pretoria, 1980, p. 18.
8. South African Nursing Council, Statistical returns for the calendar year 1985. SANA, Pretoria, 1986, C2/M86(B) p. 7.
9. South African Nursing Association, Statistics 29 January 1987.

Note
[a] Although it appears many Black nurses registered in South Africa are not practising it is likely that they are in fact practising in the National States.

Table 5 Persons on the registers and rolls of the SA Nursing Council on 31 December 1986

Category	Asian	Black	Coloured	White	Total	% of all persons on registers or rolls of SA Nursing Council
Registered nurses	1 386 (2.14%)	26 969 (41.54%)	5 737 (8.84%)	30 825 (47.48%)	64 917 (100%)	42.18
Student nurses	451 (3.15%)	7 642 (53.34%)	1 444 (10.08%)	4 791 (33.44%)	14 328 (100%)	9.31
Enrolled nurses	460 (2.06%)	14 051 (62.96%)	3 817 (17.10%)	3 990 (17.88%)	22 318 (100%)	14.50
Pupil nurses	108 (1.81%)	2 952 (49.54%)	988 (16.58%)	1 911 (32.07%)	5 959 (100%)	3.87
Enrolled nursing assistants	593 (1.41%)	25 038 (59.43%)	7 771 (18.45%)	8 726 (20.71%)	42 128 (100%)	27.38
Pupil nursing assistants	145 (3.42%)	1 973 (46.49%)	650 (15.32%)	1 476 (34.77%)	4 244 (100%)	2.76
Total	3 143	78 625	20 407	51 719	153 894	100
% of all persons on registers or rolls of SA Nursing Council	(2.04)	(51.09)	(13.26)	(33.61)	(100)	

Source
SA Nursing Council, *Statistical returns for the Calendar Year 1986*. SANC, Pretoria, 1987, C2/M87(B), C3/M87(D), C12/M87(B), C13/M87, C17/M87(A).

Note
1. An enrolled nurse has successfully completed a 2-year course (post 10 years schooling) including an SA Nursing Council final examination.
2. A pupil nurse is a trainee enrolled nurse.
3. An enrolled nursing assistant has successfully completed an in-service training programme.
4. A pupil nursing assistant is a trainee enrolled nursing assistant.

Profession should [take] immediate steps to solve the problem of recruitment, training facilities and teaching staff.[19]

There is another point to consider—the majority of health needs in South Africa are found in the community as opposed to the hospital. During their lifetime 10 per cent of the population need psychiatric care and the cause of illness in 60 per cent of all patients treated in general hospitals can be traced to psychological factors. The need for a greater number of registered nurses who have community and psychiatric nursing skills is most apparent. If we consider the scope of the registered nurses' expertise we find that currently (as at 31 December 1986) only 8.6 per cent of registered nurses are formally equipped for a community health practice and only 11.7 per cent for a psychiatric nursing practice.[20] As from January 1986 all students entering the profession will be prepared for practice in general, community and psychiatric nursing and midwifery. Further discussion of these developments will follow, but first we need to look back—where did it all begin?

The development of general nursing education

Modern professional nursing and midwifery education in South Africa dates only from 1876 although prior to this, since the days of the Batavian Republic (1803–06) and the days of the 1820 settlers, there had been sporadic attempts by concerned medical men to teach nurses and midwives. Organized nurse-training[21] schemes were only introduced into South Africa after the unprecedented social, economic and political upheaval occasioned by the diamond rush in 1866 and the later discovery of gold in 1885.[22]

Professionally trained nurses were brought in from England and in this same decade the bishops of the Anglican Diocese in Cape Town and Bloemfontein brought out devoted women of the sisterhoods to further the work of the church in South Africa in their several capacities as 'social workers', teachers and nurses. Among these was Sister Henrietta Stockdale of Kimberley, who subsequently introduced training courses for the secular women of the local community and pioneered the expansion of health practice throughout South Africa and the hinterland.[23] As the demand for medical and nursing services escalated throughout the country the need for the education and training of nurses grew more pressing.

Sister Henrietta made representations to have nurse education vested in a National Education Department and, in so doing, to separate the control of nursing education from nursing service. These representations have been repeated endlessly until finally, nearly a century later, in 1983 this goal was achieved. The nursing education programme which Sister Henrietta introduced to South Africa was based on sound educational principles which not only ensured a thorough integration of the theoretical and clinical components, but also incorporated community health through district nursing and 'welfare' work.[24]

Despite the efforts of Sister Henrietta and other nurse leaders and medical educators, nurse training developed into an apprenticeship type of training based on the Poor Law Hospitals system current in Great Britain. The regrettable result was that the service needs took first priority and students were exploited as a convenient source of inexpensive labour in the curative field, while the community aspects of prevention of illness and promotion of health were almost totally neglected—a trend which became firmly entrenched for decades.[25] Meanwhile Sister Henrietta, with the support of her peers and medical colleagues, was campaigning to gain statutory recognition for nursing through state registration and to unite the nurses of the country through a professional association. In 1891 she secured state registration of nurses and midwives—the first nurses in the world to achieve state registration. The Colonial Medical Council of the Cape became responsible for the control of nursing education.

This singular event led to further successes in the struggle for improved nursing education. With the help of eminent doctors Sister Henrietta and her followers were eventually able to persuade the four medical councils of the necessity for uniformity in training programmes, to gain the support of medical colleagues in the training of nurses and to campaign for compulsory registration and the exclusion of the non-qualified nurse from practising for gain. Sister Henrietta's efforts were not confined to the Cape Colony and her influence was paramount in training schemes throughout South Africa and in international nursing matters abroad. In 1899 the International Council of Nurses was founded with members of the provisional committee drawn from nine countries. Sister Henrietta was the member from the Cape Colony, and in 1904 Miss J. C. Child was elected as Honorary Vice-President. With this acknowledgement of the professional status of the nurses of the Cape Colony, the first links were forged in a long association of South African nurses with the International Council of Nurses and other international associations.[26] This association was terminated when

South Africa withdrew their membership from the ICN in 1973, primarily for economic reasons.[27]

Regrettably, Sister Henrietta's vision for a professional association was not realized until 1914 (three years after her death) when the South African Trained Nurses Association was inaugurated. One of the first objectives of the association was to gain representation for nurses on the medical councils and this was realized in 1928 when two nurse representatives were included on the first South African Medical Council. This was indeed a turning point as nurses and midwives now had a voice in the control of nursing education and the ethical regulation of the profession.[28]

In 1916 Afrikaans became a medium of instruction and the regulations in 1927, which prescribed syllabi, were published in both English and Afrikaans—the first time regulations were published in Afrikaans. These regulations were in line with those of the United Kingdom and the Commonwealth at that time.

In 1937, at the instigation of the SA Trained Nurses Association, the universities of Cape Town and the Witwatersrand offered a diploma in nursing which would lead to registration as a tutor. Through these two universities the doors to academic qualifications were first opened to nurses.[29]

It had always been the purpose of the nurse leaders to acquire statutory responsibility for the affairs of the profession and accordingly, in 1938, they attempted to petition Parliament for a Nursing Act but were opposed by the Medical Council.

> Four years later the Trade Union crisis in nursing circles threatened to disrupt the nursing services of the whole country and to wreck the Association's efforts to unite the nurses in a truly professional group.[30]

The SA Trained Nurses' Association (SATNA) was founded at the beginning of the First World War in a subcontinent still smouldering with economic and political unrest as an aftermath of the South African War. The leaders of the SATNA were mostly of British origin and, by the very nature of things, very senior members of the nursing hierarchy. They were required to contend with apathy in regard to nursing affairs as well as prejudice from large numbers of Afrikaans-speaking nurses. However, the trade union crisis in 1942 proved to be their finest hour.

> By the quality of their leadership . . . they gained the solid support

of the majority of nurses in the country. Once more, as in previous years, their influence extended to Members of Parliament, this time to assist them to gain statutory recognition of nurses through a Nursing Act.[31]

When the Nursing Act No. 45 of 1944 was promulgated it included in its provisions the establishment of the two independent bodies—the South African Nursing Council (SANC) to protect the interests of the public, and the South African Nursing Association (SANA) to safeguard the interests of the nursing profession. Compulsory registration with the South African Nursing Council and compulsory membership of the South African Nursing Association for all who practise for gain, brought both registered nurses and students under the ethical control of these statutory bodies.

Amongst other appointees, the Act provided for a member of the South African Medical and Dental Council (SAMDC) and this was later reciprocated by the SAMDC. The membership of the first Council was by appointment of the Minister of Health, the second and subsequent Councils have both appointed and elected members. Currently there are 30 members on the Council of whom 20 are appointed and 10 elected. At the start of the term of office of the fourth Council (in 1960) two white members were elected by Black and Coloured nurses to represent their respective interests on the Council.[32] The eighth Council (in 1979) introduced the era of representation of Black, Coloured and Indian nurses at this level, by registered nurses from their own population groups. The composition of the Council has, over the years, been based on professional expertise rather than on representation of group interests.

Since 1972, with the establishment of the Roll for nursing assistants, nobody in South Africa is allowed to practice unless he or she complies with the entrance requirements to the Register or Rolls, is in fact Registered or Enrolled with the Council and is maintaining that Registration or Enrollment through annual renewal.[33]

In South Africa there is no limit to what the nurse may do as a nurse such as there is in countries dominated by trade unions. Circumstances, social need, the conscience, the knowledge, the skills of the nurse and, above all, the immediate needs of the patient, must decide what she shall do and where, how and when she shall do it. In every one of these aspects she is held accountable to the law which gives her the right to practise. The nurse, as a registered practitioner in South Africa, is entirely responsible and accountable for her own acts and omissions to the registration authority, the South African Nursing Council, and in the broader sense to the Courts.[34] This position has not always prevailed in South Africa, however; in 1978 an amendment of major importance was introduced when the previous provision was replaced by the following:

> The registered nurse shall carry out such diagnostic and therapeutic activities as the profession permits either as an independent function, or, when applicable, under the direct or indirect supervision of a Medical Practitioner or a Dentist, or on his direction or written or verbal prescription.[35]

Even after the introduction of this new ethical provision, there remained severe restrictions upon the rights of registered nurses to perform acts amounting to what used to be regarded traditionally as 'medical acts', namely the examination of patients, the diagnosing of illness, the dispensing of medicines and the promotion of family planning. It has for a long time been felt, however, that nurses should have the right, in special circumstances, to perform some or all of these functions. In 1981 these traditional 'medical acts' were accordingly inserted into the Nursing Act No 50 1978 as section 38 A in order to make statutory provision for this expanded nursing role, one which is essential for an effective health service in a country with a scarcity of doctors, particularly in rural areas.[36] The demands of health care in South Africa require a level of responsibility from the registered nurse which far exceeds that of her Western European counterpart.

When the South African Nursing Council took over control of the profession in 1944, the nursing education system left much to be desired—facilities were inadequate, there was a dearth of textbooks and, despite the fact that there were 62 training schools for general nurses, there were only 29 tutors actively engaged in teaching of whom only six were able to teach in Afrikaans.[37] The Council made representation to the appropriate authorities in 1946 for the establishment of nursing colleges which would be affiliated to universities and for university education for nurses. It was recommended that nurse training should include the four disciplines: general, psychiatric, public health nursing and midwifery. All these recommendations were approved in principle but not implemented. The reasons for this are discussed later. Colleges of nursing were established at this time in affiliation with universities but hospitals remained the 'training schools' and thus continued to control nurse education. Although the collegiate system placed nurse education on a sounder footing, it was only in 1983 that colleges of nursing became part of the tertiary education system and, in 1986, that an association with a university nursing department became obligatory. The only exception was the University of the Orange Free State which commenced diploma nurse training under the aegis of the University Nursing Department in 1967.

The requirement (introduced in 1969) that all students entering basic nursing courses (general, psychiatric nursing and midwifery) should hold a Senior (Matriculation) Certificate (12 years schooling) was a necessary preparation for entry to tertiary education. The number of matriculated candidates had increased over the years as figures from 1960 to 1969 indicate: Blacks 11.3–27 per cent; Coloureds (and Asians) 10–18.6 per cent and Whites 25–69 per cent. By 1972 for Whites, 1973 for Blacks and 1978 for Coloureds the student enrolments exceeded those of 1969.[38] Although attrition rates have on average been lower in the post-1969 period they still remain unsatisfactorily high. Another major cause for concern is the decline in recruitment. 1986 figures for student nurses on the register show a decrease from 1979 of 36 per cent for Asian, 10 per cent for Blacks and 45 per cent for Coloureds and Whites.[39]

During the term of office of the Fifth Nursing Council (1965–70) regulations were published for the diploma for registration as a general nurse and midwife and this was followed in 1972 with regulations for the diploma in general nursing and psychiatric nursing and for the diploma in general nursing, psychiatric nursing and midwifery. This integrated approach (leading to dual or multiple registration) allows each student to be developed maximally and is also economical in time and expenditure.[40] At this time (1969) the curriculum for registrations was amended to make provision for a more comprehensive preparation of the student with regard to the basic sciences integral to nursing practice—the social, natural and biological sciences, as well as ward administration and clinical instruction.[41] The recognition of the nurse's role in rendering community health services, as opposed to curative hospital services only, is reflected in the 1975 course regulations in which 80 hours of theoretical teaching in preventive and promotive health care and family planning experience was required and examined.

In 1976 Council resolved that males be admitted to midwifery training and practice.[42] The numbers of males admitted to the register has generally been small even though their training dates back to 1915 and

1931 for White and Black students respectively.[43] Nursing in South Africa is predominantly a female profession—in 1986 96.8 per cent of nurses on the register were female.[44]

The Health Act No. 63 of 1977, which provided for a comprehensive health service, also facilitated the provision of comprehensive nursing education programmes. Arising from this Act the National Health Services Facilities Plan was approved in 1980. This plan aimed to render a health service to the community in the most cost-effective manner taking into account the availability of personnel, funds and facilities. The plan provided for 6 levels

Level 1   —provision of basic needs
Level 2   —health education
Level 3   —primary health care
Levels 4, 5 & 6—community, regional (referral hospital with basic specialist services) and academic hospitals.[45]

It is clear from this plan that nurses will be the main providers of health care.

The stage was set for a new era in nursing education and this was ushered in in 1982 when the President of the South African Nursing Association (Professor Charlotte Searle) received a letter from the Minister of Health informing her that the principle whereby universities could develop an association with nursing colleges—colleges external to the university but linked on an academic level to the university concerned—had been approved. Describing the significance of this decision Professor Searle said:

> The above decision is probably the most momentous that has been taken for the development of nursing in South Africa in this century. The establishment of nursing degree courses at South African universities was a step of major significance in the development of nursing in this country, but it must be remembered that degree courses are provided for a select few. The linking of education of all professional nurses with a university system is of the utmost importance to the profession; it will affect the professional life of all nurses, not only those who train under the new system.[46]

By September 1983 the South African Nursing Council had published the regulations for the diploma for registration as a nurse (general, psychiatric and community) and midwife with the minimum period of training being four years and with the stipulation that this new course could be offered only at a university or nursing college which had entered into an association with a university in which a department of nursing existed. These regulations became obligatory on 1 January 1986. The one-year, post-registration diploma courses in midwifery, psychiatric nursing and community nursing will, however, continue for an indefinite period.[47]

The implications of these regulations are that the responsibility for professional nurse education is now vested within the university departments of nursing—nursing education is thus no longer under the control of nursing service. Student status is, however, not regarded as synonymous with supernumerary status:

> the professional development of the nurse demands much more than the limited opportunities inherent in supernumerary status. It is imperative that the student nurse be a member of the clinical team. In order to prevent exploitation of the students' service . . . it is necessary to emphasise that the hospital should not depend entirely on student nurses for its unregistered nursing service requirements.[48]

Students registered with the college, and their clinical placements, are the responsibility of the college. The examinations (theoretical and clinical) are local and moderated by the university instead of being national South African Nursing Council examinations. Because of the diversity of clinical experience required by these students, nurse educators have been meeting with their colleagues in the various spheres of nursing practice to an unprecedented degree. The mutual understanding and co-operation which has resulted can only augur well for the future.

The new curriculum, in providing for the comprehensive preparation of the nurse (general, psychiatric and community) and midwife, lays a sound foundation for the future practitioner, the professional nurse who will be at the peak of her career by the year 2000.

The development of midwifery training programmes

Traditionally in South Africa, as in many Western countries, the training of midwives has been accorded priority and, indeed, the first school for midwives was established in 1810. The regulations for the conduct of the midwifery school were remarkable in that they contained concepts which today are considered as essential principles underlying a sound educational programme and the provision of an efficient and adequate nursing service.[49]

Professional midwifery education and practice was introduced throughout the country by the end of the nineteenth century. With a sparsely distributed population, and with insufficient doctors to meet the obstetric needs of the community, an urgent need existed (and indeed still exists today) for the training of midwives. Initially there were no lying-in hospitals or wards, and midwifery training started as a district midwifery service. When a maternity ward was established at the Kimberley Hospital (before the mid-1890s) training was done both on the district and in the wards. In time this became the accepted pattern for the training of midwives.

Up to 1940 the facilities for the training of midwives were not adequate, even though a number of schools existed.[50] During 1946–8 the system of voluntary public hospitals was replaced by hospitals run by the provincial administrations which included the provision of midwifery beds and, later, district midwifery services as well. This had a significant impact on the improvement of facilities for the training of nurses. In addition, subsidies were granted to mission and certain other private hospitals to provide services and to train nurses and midwives in the remote areas.[51]

In 1949 the South African Nursing Council increased training to 9 months for registered nurses and 18 months for those who were not trained nurses, and by July 1960 this had changed to 12 and 24 months respectively. By 1960 81 per cent of student midwives were registered as nurses prior to their admission to training as midwives, and thus by 1972, the two-year midwifery course had served its purpose and was discontinued.[52]

Towards the end of 1969 new regulations were published for the diploma for registration as general nurse and as a midwife. In view of the combined general nurse and midwife diploma the training period was reduced to three-and-a-half years instead of three years general and one year midwifery.[53] These regulations paved the way for the integrated course which is offered today in which general, psychiatric and community nursing and midwifery preparation are provided in the curriculum of all student nurses. Today 80 per cent of all registered nurses are registered as midwives as well. The midwifery courses offered for registration as a midwife are either a one-year diploma course for registered nurses or the integrated diploma or degree courses of four years' duration leading to multiple basic registrations. The four-year diploma course is offered in association with a university nursing department. In addition, a one-year post-registration advanced course in midwifery and neonatal nursing science is offered and graduates can pursue programmes at masters' and doctoral levels.

Table 6   Percentage of Black, Coloured, Indian and White student nurses on basic courses[a] (nurses & midwives) approved by the SA Nursing Council (as at 31 December)

Year	Student group: % of the total				
	Asian	Black	Coloured	White	Total (%)
1963		35.74	8.85	55.41	100
1967		41.78	14.29	43.93	100
1969		42.92	14.31	42.77	100
1971		44.01	10.65	45.34	100
1973	2.38[b]	43.93	7.66	46.03	100
1984	3.29	54.82	12.08	29.81	100
1986	3.43	55.91	10.43	30.23	100

Source
1. South African Nursing Association, The Board, *Nursing Education in the Republic of South Africa*. SANA, Pretoria, 1976, pp. 17, 88, 108, 153.
2. South African Nursing Council, *Statistical returns for the calendar year 1985*. SANC, Pretoria, 1986, C3/M86(B) & (D).
3. South African Nursing Council, *Statistical returns for the calendar year 1986*. SANC, Pretoria, 1987, C3/M87(B) & (D).
Note
[a]These figures do not include degree and diploma students at universities.
[b]Prior to 1973 statistics for Asian students were included with those of the Coloured student nurses.

The development of psychiatric nursing

In the early nineteenth century when cruelty to the insane was common in Europe, the South African records show little evidence of physical cruelty. Only those who were dangerous to themselves and to others were locked up or removed to the settlement on Robben Island. In South Africa the insane were regarded as persons with rights and as human beings with souls—these being basic concepts of Roman-Dutch Law.[54]

Training for attendants and nurses was first introduced in 1891, leading to examination and certification under the auspices of the Medico-Psychological Association of Great Britain. Progress in this sphere of practice was retarded for many years due to economic and

Table 7 Registration of midwives/accouchers—number of persons on the Register of the South African Council (as at 31 December 1986)

Registration	Asian	Black	Coloured	White	Total	Percentage of total number registered midwives/accouchers
1. *General nurse & midwife/accoucheur*	1 148	21 664	4 983	22 085	49 880	95.93
General nurse and midwife/accoucheur	985	19 508	4 524	18 606	43 623	
General nurse, psychiatric nurse and midwife/accoucheur	162	2 152	456	3 161	5 931	
General nurse, mental nurse and midwife	1	4	3	34	42	
General nurse, nurse for mental defectives and midwife	–	–	–	2	2	
Nurse (general, psychiatric and community) and midwife/accoucheur	–	–	–	282	282	
2. *Psychiatric (or mental nurse) and midwife*	–	1	–	14	15	0.03
Psychiatric nurse and midwife	–	1	–	4	5	
Mental nurse and midwife	–	–	–	8	8	
Nurse for mental defectives and midwife	–	–	–	2	2	
3. *Midwife/accoucheur*	32	1 665	130	276	2 103	4.04
Midwife	4	157	101	254	516	
Midwife/accoucheur and enrolled nurse	28	1 504	29	11	1 572	
Midwife and enrolled nursing assistant	–	4	–	11	15	
		Total number of persons registered as midwives/accouchers			51 998	100
		% of total registered nurses			(80.1)	

Source 1. SA Nursing Council, *Statistical returns for the calendar year 1986.* SANC, Pretoria, 1987, C2/M87 (B) political disturbances and cultural differences and, even after 1910 when the Provincial Medical Councils introduced courses for training and examination of mental nurses, very few took advantage of the opportunity to enter for the local examination.

In 1929 a course for training and examination of nurses for mental defectives was introduced by the South African Medical Council but it was not until recognition of the British qualification was withdrawn in 1932 that the local examining body—the South African Medical Council—acquired recognition.[55] Regrettably, the total lack of an organized educational system, the low standard of education of recruits and lack of job satisfaction made, of mental nursing, a virtual Cinderella service until 1954 when the SA Nursing Council promulgated regulations for training and examination of psychiatric nurses, improving the syllabus and holding out more opportunity for staff rotation and promotion. Unfortunately the Department of Health and the mental hospitals did not introduce this course until 1964. Up to 1964 the Physician-Superintendent of the hospital was designated as the person in charge of the nursing school, despite repeated representations by the South African Trained Nurses Association and its successor the SA Nursing Association, as well as the SA Nursing Council. As a result, nurses' training remained an apprenticeship with training needs secondary to the labour needs of the hospital, resulting in a breakdown in the mental nursing services. Psychiatrists did not acknowledge the importance of the mental health nurse in the therapeutic team with the result that educational programmes made little progress.[56]

A major reorganization in the system of training occurred during the mid-1960s and the first tutors qualified at the end of 1965. By the end of 1969, 18 tutors and 36 psychiatric nurse instructors had qualified, and the number of psychiatric nurses far exceeded the number of mental nurses.[57] Another milestone was that the first mental nurse was admitted to the hospital and health services administration course (at the University of the Orange Free State) in the mid-1960s—thus opening the way for nurse administrators in the mental health field.[58]

In 1952 post-registration courses, namely the certificate in psychiatric and neurological nursing and the diploma course for the psychiatric nurse instructor, were introduced, the latter opening the door for promotion to the posts of head nurse and matron and securing for the nurse a place in the management team.[59] In 1966 a post-registration course was introduced which provided for in-depth study in psychiatry within the context of the diploma in nursing education. An intensive campaign was also launched by the State Health Department to improve

Table 8   Psychiatric nurses, mental nurses and nurses for mental defectives: number of persons on the registers as at 31 December (all races)

Category	1933	1943	1953	1969	1974	1985
Mental nurses	⎫	⎫	⎫	448	320	196
Nurses for mental defectives	⎬ 803	⎬ 940	⎬ 1 308	68	59	23
Mental nurse and nurse for mental defectives	–	–	–	3	–	–
Psychiatric nurse	–	–	–	1 624	2 504	7 131
Total	803	940	1 308	2 143	2 883	7 350
% of total registrations	12.32	6.72	5.3	5.61	6.62	11.53

Sources
1. Searle, C., *The history of the development of nursing in South Africa 1652–1960*. SA Nursing Association, Pretoria, 1965, p. 265.
2. SA Nursing Council, *Report of the Sixth Council 1970–1975*. SANC, Pretoria, 1976, Annexure E.
3. SA Nursing Council, *Statistical returns for the Calendar Year 1985*. SANC, Pretoria, 1986, C2M86 (B).

nursing education programmes in psychiatric hospitals by the establishment of six central teaching hospitals and two decentralized teaching centres.

Finally the SA Nursing Council's introduction of the senior certificate as an admission requirement for all basic diploma courses in 1969 and the introduction in the same year of integrated courses at diploma and degree levels leading to a dual (general and midwifery) or multiple (general, midwifery and psychiatric nursing) registration set psychiatric nursing on a much improved footing.[60] By the end of 1986 11.7 per cent of nurses on the register were psychiatric nurses and 0.3 per cent were mental nurses or nurses for mental defectives. The latter two courses were discontinued in 1970.[61]

Clearly, in the past two decades psychiatric nursing and nursing education in this field have made tremendous strides, as is numerically reflected in Tables 8 and 9. The inclusion of psychiatric nursing in the curricula of the integrated courses of the South African Nursing Council and the closer co-operation between the State and Provincial Health authorities are providing momentum for progress in mental health in its entirety.[62]

Today psychiatric nurses are unquestionably an integral part of the therapeutic team with recognized professional expertise. The advent of post-registration advanced diplomas in psychiatric nursing specialties, master's and doctoral degree programmes has resulted in a cadre of

Table 9   Registration of psychiatric nurses, mental nurses, nurses for mental defectives—number of persons on the register of the South African Nursing Council as at 31 December 1969 and 1986

Capacity/capacities in which registered	1969						1986					
	Asian	Black	Coloured	White	Totals	% Total	Asian	Black	Coloured	White	Totals	% of Total
Single registration												
Psychiatric nurse	–	285	40	1 079	1 404		11	281	55	406	753	
Mental nurse	–	61	3	209	273		–	5	–	75	80	
Nurse for mental defectives	–	–	2	28	30	1 707 79.65%	–	–	1	17	18	851 10.9%
Dual registration												
General nurse and psychiatric nurse	–	11	1	46	58		15	290	31	287	623	
General nurse and mental nurse	–	7	4	71	82		–	2	–	56	58	
General nurse and nurse for mental defectives	–	–	–	14	14		–	–	–	3	3	
Psychiatric nurse and midwife	–	1	–	12	13		–	1	–	4	5	
Mental nurse and midwife	–	–	–	30	30		–	–	–	8	8	
Nurse for mental defectives and midwife	–	–	–	11	11		–	–	–	2	2	
Psychiatric and neurological nursing (post-basic)	–	–	–	20	20	228 10.64%	–	–	–	2	2	699 8.95%
Multiple registration												
Nurse (general, psychiatric and community) and midwife	34	–	2	93	129		–	–	–	282	282	
General nurse, psychiatric nurse and midwife/accoucheur							162	2 152	456	3 161	5 931	
General nurse, mental nurse and nurse for mental defectives	–	–	–	3	3		–	–	–	–	–	
General nurse, mental nurse and midwife	6	–	3	54	63		1	4	3	34	42	
General nurse, nurse for mental defectives and midwife	–	–	–	13	13	208 9.71%	–	–	–	2	2	6 257 80.15%
Total number of persons registered	40	365	55	1 683	2 143		189	2 735	546	4 337	7 807	100%
% of total registered nurses (as at 31 December)						5.61						
Total number of:	Asian	Black	Coloured	White	Total	% Total	Asian	Black	Coloured	White	Total	% of Total
Psychiatric nurses	34	297	43	1 250	1 624	75.78	188	2 724	542	4 140	7 594	97.3
Mental nurses	6	68	10	364	448	20.91	1	11	3	173	188	2.4
Nurses for mental defectives	–	–	2	66	68	3.17	–	–	1	24	25	0.3
Mental nurses and nurses for mental defectives	–	–	–	3	3	0.14	–	–	–	–	–	–
					2 143	100					7 807	100

Sources
1. SA Nursing Council, *Report of the Sixth Council 1970–1975*. SANC, Pretoria, 1976, Annexure E.
2. SA Nursing Council, *Statistical returns for the calendar year 1986*. SANC, Pretoria, 1987, C2/M87(B).

nurse leadership in this field which is crucial to the future of mental health care in South Africa.

University education for nurses, 1956–87

Introduction: university education for women

Although the first women to be admitted to undergraduate study entered the South African College in 1886 it was not until 1887 that the Council, satisfied with the experiment, resolved: 'that the gates of the College be thrown wide to women in honour of Queen Victoria's Diamond Jubilee'.[63] Writing about the 1918s a student leader said: 'women had to fight for everything . . . there were seven of us who were a group . . . there was only nursing or teaching'.[64] Although nursing was one of the two main professions open to women, and although the doors to university education for nurses were opened in 1937 when the first diploma courses leading to registration as a tutor were offered at the universities of Cape Town and Witwatersrand, the development of nursing education to graduate level was slow. The reasons for this must initially be sought in the general education system which in its turn compounded the problem in the development of nursing education. Although the desirability of academic preparation for nurses was recognized 80 years ago in South Africa, the progression towards university education for nurses has been hampered by a number of factors, some of which are listed below:

(1) poor general education and economic stringency, and competition for those suitably educated;
(2) shortage of teachers of mathematics, science and biology;
(3) failure on the part of educators and parents to recognize the need to educate girls at least to matriculation level.[65]

In 1944 representations were made by the South African Nursing Council to the universities, the Minister of Health and the Provincial Authorities in order to establish a comprehensive education for nurses within the universities in all four disciplines, namely general, psychiatric, public health and midwifery. At the same time the Nursing Council identified the need for the appointment of Professors of Nursing at the universities and Directresses of Nursing Services in the Provincial Departments of Hospital Services. The importance of these recommendations was recognized by all concerned but they were unable to implement them due to an inadequate statutory provision for comprehensive health services and, consequently, the provision of comprehensive nursing education programmes; the absence of a national policy on nursing education; the fact that nursing education was controlled by nursing service (the hospital nursing school system) and the concept of service for education which was strongly adhered to throughout the profession.[66]

Undergraduate nursing education at university level (generic degrees for entry to the profession) and post-graduate education

The event which has had the most significant effect on nursing and nursing education, particularly during these three decades, and which will continue to play a central role in nursing in the next century, is the establishment of university departments of nursing and degree courses for nurses at universities.

The first degree course for nurses (which led to registration as a nurse) was commenced at the University of Pretoria in 1956. A four-and-a-half year BA (Nursing) degree course was offered in the Faculty of Arts, through the Afrikaans medium in co-operation with the Transvaal Provincial Administration who made 35 scholarships available annually. These scholarships (from which tuition fees and other costs were met) were tenable for the duration of the course and were equivalent to the annual training allowance (salary) for student nurses following the South African Nursing Council diploma course for registration as a nurse.[67]

The first Chair of Nursing endowed by the South African Nursing Association was established within the Medical Faculty at Pretoria University in 1967, and Professor Charlotte Searle was appointed to this historic position.[68] At this time the course moved from the Arts Faculty to the Medical Faculty and the title of the degree was changed to Baccalaureus Curationis (BCur). In adopting the term 'Curationis' for the nursing degree,

the Medical Faculty accepted the fact that nursing has a healing art function of its own in addition to that which it applies under medical direction, and that the nurse is in reality a nurse practitioner in the fullest sense.[69]

The establishment of further degree courses followed that of Pretoria University: in 1962 the University of Natal (Durban) offered the first course in English, a Bachelor of Social Science (Nursing) degree and, also in 1962, the University of the Orange Free State (Bloemfontein) followed suit again offering a degree in the Social Science Faculty. The establishment of a Bachelor of Nursing degree in the Medical Faculty at the University of Stellenbosch (Cape) in 1963 meant that each province would have undergraduate programmes which led to professional registration as a nurse. With the advent of university nursing departments the responsibility for nursing education was removed from nursing service—a trend which is only gaining momentum in the mid-1980s in the wider profession. By 30 June 1964 the students on degree courses represented approximately 1.59 per cent of all students preparing for the register (nurse or midwife). In addition, there were at this time 56 graduates from Pretoria University.[70]

As the degree students received scholarships (study grants) from the respective Provincial Administrations it meant that the intake of students was (and continues to be) fixed according to the number of scholarships available. Additional scholarships are required as suitable applicants are regularly being turned down due to the lack of study grants.

An event which had a serious impact on university education (including nursing education) in South Africa was the extension of the University Education Act No. 45 of 1959. Up to then the university was open to all who met the academic requirements for entry. In 1959 legislation prevented students who were not White from attending the university without the special permission of a Minister of State (the only exceptions were the University of South Africa which teaches by correspondence and the Medical School of the University of Natal). This permission was normally granted only where provision was not available to enable Black South African students to study the subject of their choice in one of the universities established for Blacks only. From the time when this legislation was first mooted, the universities of Cape Town and the Witwatersrand opposed it. Both these universities—their chancellors, principals, councils, senates, lecturers, students and former students—contested every step which the government took to place its plan in the statute book, as did many other organizations and the parliamentary opposition, but the Bill was passed. Despite continued representation from both these universities a 'permit system' operated from 1959 until the relevant sections of the Act were repealed in 1983. It was then replaced with a system which empowered the Minister of National Education to impose a limit or 'quota' on the number of Blacks at what some choose to call the White universities.

The minister has, however, not imposed any quotas on the universities.[71]

Since 1985 there have been no restrictions on admission to study at universities in South Africa on the grounds of race or population group as defined by law. The statutory provisions allowing the minister to set restrictions remain, but thus far the minister has not used these.[72]

University departments of nursing were, as has already been indicated, linked to their respective Provincial Administration which, in addition to providing generous student scholarships and in some instances subsidizing academic posts, also provided access to their hospitals and health services essential for the clinical education of the degree student. Under this 1959 Act it became, at that time, almost impossible for students who were not White to enter a degree course in nursing. Although a permit was required to study at a White university this did not present an insurmountable problem, but securing the necessary clinical opportunities often did. Another stumbling block for Black students has been the poor secondary school education about which the South African Nursing Association has made strong and repeated representation to the appropriate authorities.[73]

The creation of university departments of nursing required suitable academic personnel and literature relevant to the national situation and available in the language of the students. The challenge to nurse educationists was enormous, many of whom needed to obtain first and higher degrees, to undertake research and to write, whilst at the same time launching and promoting degree courses (under- and postgraduate) for nurses as well as university-based diploma courses for leaders, particularly in nursing administration and nursing education.

Carlyle says 'no great man lives in vain. The history of the world is but the biography of great men'.[74] The nursing history of South Africa is indeed the biography of great women and men.

Writing in 1966 Charlotte Searle said:

> If the nursing profession is to keep pace with developments in medical science and practice at least 25% of all professional nurses should receive their basic preparation at degree level.[75]

The establishment of two further university departments of nursing at Potchefstroom University in 1966 and the University of Witwatersrand in 1969 (BSc Nursing) brought to a total of six the number of bachelors' degree courses. In addition, a three-year diploma in nursing was commenced at the University of Orange Free State in 1967—this was the first diploma course for registration as a nurse to be offered at university level.

Thus in 1969 11.3 per cent (as opposed to 4.3 per cent in 1966) of all White student nurses (excluding student midwives) were now receiving their basic nursing education—degree and diploma—at a university. This represents 4.15 per cent of all student nurses.[76] South African nurses have received magnificent co-operation and support from all the major universities in the country. Financially the universities have faced heavy costs and the profession has cause for much gratitude to the universities who shouldered the financial burden of the nursing education programmes.

In 1969 the second Chair of Nursing in South Africa was established at the University of the Orange Free State and, currently, there are 15 departments of nursing of which 13 offer basic (generic) degrees and have Chairs of Nursing. In 1970 the universities of Pretoria and Orange Free State introduced a four-and-a-half-year basic nursing degree course which led to triple registration as a general nurse, psychiatric nurse and midwife, and the latter university also started a four-year basic nursing diploma course on the same lines. In the same year the University of the Orange Free State, in collaboration with the Department of Health, approved the first basic university course for male students in South Africa who commenced the course at the beginning of 1971. These male students would, on completion of their training, register as general, psychiatric and orthopaedic nurses.[77]

In 1976, 6.7 per cent of all student nurses were on degree courses.[78] By 1986, 17.7 per cent of White, 5.8 per cent of Coloured, 0.9 per cent of Asiatic and 4.5 per cent of Black students were studying at universities: a total of 8.9 per cent.[79] There is still a long way to go to realize the goal of 25 per cent of professional nurses receiving their basic preparation at degree level but it is encouraging that studies have shown that these graduates remain in the profession and contribute significantly to it.[80]

The need exists not only for generic degrees but for post-registration degrees as well. The future of generic degrees was, and still remains, inextricably linked to a cadre of nurse leadership drawn from the ranks of nurses who hold post-registration degrees. The first such degree course was introduced at Pretoria University in 1970 and led to registration in the additional qualifications of nursing education (tutor) and nursing administration. At this time nine universities offered diploma courses in nursing education and two offered diploma courses in nursing

Table 10   Students on undergraduate nursing degree courses at South African universities (as at 31 December unless otherwise indicated)

University and date of commencement of course	1956	1964 (as at 30/6)	1966 (as at 31/8)	1968 (as at 31/5)	1969	1971	1973	1974	1975	1976	1981 (as at 31/12)	1984	1985	1986
Pretoria (1956)	32	114	105	116	97	150	150	148	119	131				
Natal (1962)	–	20	26	37	39	68	69	70	54	48				
Orange Free State (1962)	–	11	15	24	18	64	145	180	228	249				
Stellenbosch (1963)	–	13	31	51	58	76	90	100	103	129				
Potchefstroom (1966)	–	–	8	35	46	59	73	66	76	66				
Witwatersrand (1969)	–	–	–	–	10	38	49	54	32	37				
Cape Town (1972)	–	–	–	–	–	–	15	13	20	25				
				–White	–Coloured									
				Coloured					2	2				
				Indian						1				
Western Cape (1972)					–	–	20	36	27	28				
Port Elizabeth (1975)							–	–	5	24				
Rand Afrikaans (1975)							–	–	16	30				
Zululand (1984)										Black	–	30	62	
Medunsa (1981)										Black	10	68	69	
Total White	0	158	185	263	268	455	591	631	653	739	1 130	1 012	1 001	1 281
Coloured							20	36	29	30	26			
Indian										1	3			
Black											13			
TOTAL	0	158	185	263	268	455	611	667	682	770	1 172	1 012	1 001	1 281

Sources
1. South African Nursing Association, *Nursing Education in the Republic of South Africa 1914–1974*. SANA, Pretoria, 1975, pp. 25, 48, 84, 131, 162.
2. South African Nursing Association, *Report on Nursing Education in the Republic of South Africa and Self-Governing Territories*. SANA, Pretoria, 1978, pp. 10, 32.
3. South African Nursing Association, *Report of the Nursing Service and Nursing Education in the Republic of South Africa 1979–1983*. SANA, Pretoria, 1985, p. 32.
4. R. Thompson, correspondence with heads of nursing departments.
5. South African Nursing Council, *Statistical returns for the calendar year 1985*. SANA, Pretoria, 1986, C3/M86(B).
6. South African Nursing Council, *Statistical returns for the calendar year 1986*. SANA, Pretoria, 1987, C3/M87(B).

administration.[81] In addition, four universities offered masters' degrees in nursing and Pretoria University offered a doctoral degree (DCur). During the early 1970s some universities also offered community nursing science as a major subject in their post-basic degrees and as a specialty in their post-graduate programmes.

By March 1986, 1047 registered nurses had received post-registration bachelors' degrees, 151 honours, 136 masters and 26 doctoral degrees had been awarded. Of this total of 1360, 27.65 per cent had been awarded by 14 residential universities and the rest (72.35 per cent) over the past 11 years, by the University of South Africa.[82] Post-graduate nurse education is the cornerstone of a research-based profession. Nursing research is still in its infancy but is developing rapidly.

The University of South Africa

The University of South Africa (UNISA) is a non-residential university teaching by tele-tuition (distance education) through the printed word and through a bilingual medium to an international student body. UNISA has a student body of approximately 90 000 (1987) of whom 5 per cent are studying full-time. Most are mature persons of whom 57.3 per cent are married and more than 80 per cent are in full-time employment. UNISA is distinguished from other universities by its non-residential, cross-cultural character, its method of tuition and the fact that it offers opportunities for post-registration studies in nursing through tele-tuition. Few, if any, universities internationally offer a range similar to UNISA's nursing studies.

The expanding health services of the country, the shortage of senior personnel with suitable post-registration qualifications and the inability of many practising nurses to enrol in residential full-time courses— either for domestic reasons or because the relevant authorities were unable to release them from their posts—were the reasons underlying the requests for the introduction of correspondence courses for nurses. Nurse leaders considered it imperative that large numbers of personnel be academically prepared as rapidly as possible to fill key positions in the health services. This was impossible to achieve with normal full-time residential courses. In addition, the correspondence courses meet a pressing need for Black nurses for whom facilities for further study are both inadequate in number and inappropriate. Many have domestic ties in rural areas and are quite unable to study full-time at the existing institutions, which are mostly located in the cities.

The Department of Nursing at UNISA was established in 1975 and

Professor Charlotte Searle was appointed as head. The first students registered in 1976. There are two curricula for a bachelors' degree, both have two majors: one being community health nursing science and the second being a choice of either nursing administration or nursing education. Each major comprises three courses. The other courses are selected from a number of options, to make a total of eleven courses. The nature of these courses gives the nurse an opportunity to improve and broaden her education. As at March 1986 some 876 (see Table 11) nurses have graduated and registration figures were 4234. A BCur honours degree comprising five nursing courses is also offered. The masters' and doctoral degrees comprise a dissertation or thesis on any approved subject in the field of nursing.

Table 11   Total number of nursing degrees awarded by universities in South Africa as at March 1986

University	Bachelors' degree	Post-basic bachelors	Honours degree	Masters' degree	Doctoral degree	Total
Medunsa	6	22	–	–	–	28
Potchefstroom	163	–	–	3	5	171
Rand Afrikaans	99	42	–	12	1	154
University of Cape Town	80	–	–	0	–	80
Fort Hare	0	0	–	0	0	0
Natal	204	–	20	–	–	224
North	–	26	–	–	–	26
Orange Free State	503	–	–	38	1	542
Pretoria	550	49	15	50	4	668
Port Elizabeth	87	24	3	12	3	129
South Africa	–	876	84	15	9	984
Stellenbosch	328	–	26	1	3	358
Western Cape	42	0	3	0	0	45
Witwatersrand	106	–	–	5	0	111
Zululand	0	8	–	–	–	8
Total	2 168 (61.4%)	1 047 (29.7%)	151 (4.3%)	136 (3.8%)	26 (0.7%)	3 528

Key: – = Do not award these degrees.
      0 = No degrees yet awarded.

Sources
1. Van Niekerk, J. G. P., 'Verpleegkunde: 30 jaar van Graadopleiding in Suid Afrika', *Human Sciences Research Council Research Bulletin*, 1986, **16**, No. 5, 33.
2. Correspondence with Head, Department of Nursing of the University of the North, University of Fort Hare, University of Zululand, February 1987.

Registrations from non-White students are more than double those of the White students and while, initially, students were drawn from the ranks of the older experienced nurses, the student age has decreased and today students are mostly younger and less professionally mature. As all are post-registration courses proof of current registration as a general nurse with the South African Nursing Council (or their own country's registration authority in the case of foreign students) is essential. Current membership of the South African Nursing Association is essential for purposes of professional indemnity, before undertaking the required clinical practica. The university is entirely dependent upon the Provincial and State Health Authorities and their staff who act as supervisors in the field for the various practica required.[83]

The contribution of the Department of Nursing at UNISA to nurses and to nursing in South Africa is considerable and the opportunity to study by tele-tuition is invaluable. The racial imbalance in the development of generic degrees for nurses has been significantly redressed by the post-basic degrees offered by UNISA. However, it is also important that solutions be found to increase the enrolments at residential universities despite the economic disadvantage which students at residential universities experience compared with those studying through UNISA.

If the graduates from generic degrees are to reach the goal of 25 per cent of the profession then:

South African universities must become 'user friendly' to those young people who have suffered serious educational and social disadvantages . . . the standard at the end must remain unchanged . . . but the admission criteria must obviously be adapted to recognise potential, rather than past achievements. This is difficult to accomplish and the matter needs urgent study and evaluation . . . . . . A university is a special place, constituted by specially selected people for a very special purpose; it should not merely reflect events in the country, but should point the way how the country should and could develop. The campus is a signpost not a mirror.[84]

The same is true for university nursing departments. Professional nurse education, and thus a significant part of the future health care of the nation, rests with them—an awesome responsibility for a small group of nurse leaders.

Post-basic nursing education

The direction which post-basic (post-registration) education for nurses has taken at diploma, graduate and post-graduate level can be grouped as follows: clinical field; education; administration. In all of these, nurses are involved in nursing research at an appropriate level. Post-basic courses which are at least equivalent to one year of full-time study, and other requirements of the South African Nursing Council, are registrable. Shorter (certificate) courses are listed but not registered by the South African Nursing Council. The profession thus has a clear profile of the extent of 'specialization' amongst its registered nurse population. Such a profile is invaluable when undertaking nurse manpower studies and planning health services.

Currently the contribution of private hospitals to the health services is escalating rapidly. Most of these hospitals specialize in diagnostic and surgical cases and are often better equipped with specialized apparatus than are some of the academic hospitals.[85] These hospitals at present do not contribute to professional nurse education but are 'consumers' of specialized nurse manpower.

Conclusion—looking ahead

In looking at the education of the professional nurse for tomorrow's health, it seems that to contemplate improvements in curriculum design is to contemplate only the lesser problem in educating clinical personnel. My concern is much more with the nature of the academic and clinical experience, its meaning and its value for the student attempting to develop her (or his) potential as a human being and in her profession. It seems we need to develop concepts of education in which students gain carefully timed and graduated experience in exploring and exercising their professional programme.

It is clear that many education programmes require reorientation if nurses are to develop the skills for planning and providing the kind of nursing practice which is so urgently required if contemporary and future health-care needs are to be met. The shift in the education of the nurse should be towards a person- and health-centred approach. How does one achieve this? It requires that the programme of nurse education is person- and health-oriented. This necessitates an emphasis on individual, family and community health.

Because the family unit is a microcosm of society it reflects accurately

Table 12 Post-basic (post-registration) qualifications on the register of the South African Nursing Council: 1953–86

Course	Date first commenced	1953 Total no.	1953 % White	1964 Total no.	1964 % Asian	1964 % Black	1964 % Coloured	1964 % White	1974 Total no.	1974 % Asian	1974 % Black	1974 % Coloured	1974 % White	1986 Total no.	1986 % Asian	1986 % Black	1986 % Coloured	1986 % White
Nursing administration	1951	7	100	155	–	–	–	100	500	–	5.2	2.4	92.4	2 159	1.5	39.3	4.9	54.3
Nursing education	1935	147	100	381	–	4.7	1.3	94	831	–	12.8	7.9	79.3	2 068	1.8	33.8	6.9	57.5
Clinical courses:																		
1. Advanced midwifery & nursing science	1979	–	–	–	–	–	–	–	–	–	–	–	–	196	6.6	64.3	9.2	19.9
2. Advanced paediatric & neonatal nursing science	1981	–	–	–	–	–	–	–	–	–	–	–	–	–	–	–	–	–
3. Advanced psychiatric nursing science	1979	–	–	–	–	–	–	–	–	–	–	–	–	18	–	–	27.8	72.2
5. Community nursing science[a]	1980	214	100	884[a]	–	26.7	6.0	67.3	296[b]	3.0	33.4	19.3	44.3	5 328	2.9	35.1	10.1	51.9
6. General nurse instructor	1978	–	–	–	–	–	–	–	–	–	–	–	–	121	–	81.8	10.7	7.5
7. Geriatric nursing science	1979	–	–	–	–	–	–	–	–	–	–	–	–	–	–	–	–	–
8. Intensive nursing science	?1972	–	–	–	–	–	–	–	332	0.9	22.9	5.1	71.1	1 665	2.1	28.3	10.0	59.6
9. Oncological nursing science	1981	–	–	–	–	–	–	–	–	–	–	–	–	91	2.2	38.5	15.4	43.9
10. Operating theatre techniques	1953	–	–	392	–	10.0	2.0	88.0	1 312	–	27.9	4.3	67.8	2 824	1.2	35.7	5.2	57.9
11. Ophthalmic nursing science	1955	–	–	31	–	80.7	3.2	16.1	156	–	77.6	1.9	20.5	318	2.8	82.1	3.8	11.3
12. Orthopaedic nursing science	1941	46	100	114	–	4.4	5.3	90.3	376	–	49.0	5.3	45.7	830	1.1	51.6	8.6	38.7
13. Paediatric nursing science[c]	1952	8	100	122	–	0.8	0.8	98.4	537	0.4	27.0	7.0	65.6	1 488	1.4	46.7	11.7	40.2
14. Psychiatric nursing science	1965	–	–	–	–	–	–	–	not available					7 594	2.5	35.9	7.1	54.5

Sources

1. Searle, C., *The History of the Development of Nursing in South Africa 1652–1960*. SA Nursing Association, Pretoria, 1965. p. 345.
2. SA Nursing Council, *Report of the Sixth Council, 1 April 1970–31 March 1975*. SANC, Pretoria, 1977, pp. 1 & 2, 49–51.
3. SA Nursing Association, The Board, *Nursing Education in the Republic of South Africa 1914–1974*. SANA, Pretoria, 1976, pp. 40–41.
4. SA Nursing Council, *Report of the Fifth Council, 1 April 1965–31 March 1970*. SANC, Pretoria, 1971, pp. 69 & 70.
5. SA Nursing Council, *Report of the Seventh Council, 1 April 1975–31 March 1979*. SANC, Pretoria, 1980, pp. 75–78.
6. SA Nursing Council, *Report of the Eighth Council, 1 April 1979–31 March 1984*. SANC, Pretoria, 1986, pp. 34–51.
7. SA Nursing Council, *Statistical returns for the calendar year 1986*. SANC, Pretoria, 1987, C2/M 86(J).

Notes

1. Current course titles are given.
2. These figures relate to additional qualifications on the registers and not persons. One person may have one or more additional qualifications.

[a] Health visiting and school nursing course commenced 1925 and discontinued 1970; district nursing course commenced 1970 and discontinued 1979.

[b] Public health nursing (health visiting, school, district, occupational health care and mothercraft) commenced 1970 and discontinued 1980. (Prior to this a fever course was offered.)

[c] Mothercraft course commenced 1924 and discontinued 1975. (Figures not included 1953 (289); 1974 (468).)

the needs of society at large. The family is the social unit of concern and, therefore, the basic unit for determining health progress. Social values, health behaviours and health perceptions are family-oriented and transmitted and, therefore, any significant change in individual and group behaviour must also have a family orientation.

If the hospital is seen as the pivotal unit it becomes the total focus and everything else is peripheral. If the home (family) is presented as the pivotal unit then the hospital is seen as a means of returning the person to that unit in society rather than as an end in itself.

The aim of the nursing service, which has for a very long time been centred solely on the concepts of disease, functional disorders and maladjustment, must now turn towards the development of the belief in the capacity of individuals and groups to use their potential for living in all its dimensions. In so doing, nurses will help to promote the ability of each human being and the ability of families and the community to become more autonomous in identifying and meeting their health needs and in utilizing the health services, rather than merely strengthening the accumulation of health knowledge.

The nurse of the future needs to be a motivator, facilitator, teacher and communicator in the field of health. These skills are generally underestimated and underdeveloped in most spheres of nursing. The nurse of the future must be more than a 'hospital nurse'. While we will always need nurses to give direct care to the sick in institutional settings, we must redress the balance without allowing this to dominate our entire view of what nursing is about.

We cannot conceive all the changes which lie ahead. We therefore need a profession which remains faithful to the enduring responsibilities which lie at the heart of nursing, but at the same time one which accepts the necessities and virtues of adapting quickly and intelligently.[87] Perhaps it is salutary to conclude with Florence Nightingale's wise words:

> For us who nurse, our nursing is the thing which, unless in it we are making progress every year, every month, every week, take my word for it, we are going back. The more experience gained, the more progress we can make . . . after all, all that our training can do for us is to teach us to train ourselves.[88]

References

1. Mahler, H. as quoted by Fulop, T., 'The future of W.H.O.'s Health Manpower Development Programme', *WHO Chronicle*, 1982, **36**, 3.

2. Report of the Science Committee of the President's Council, *Demographic Trends in South-Africa*. Government Printer, Cape Town, 1983, pp. 8, 12.
3. Behr, A. L., *New Perspectives in South African Education*. Butterworths, Durban, 1978. (Reprinted supplement 1980.) Quoted in Mashaba, T. G., *The Education and Training of the Black Nurse in South Africa 1900–1982*. University of South Africa, Pretoria, 1985, p. 15. (Thesis DLitt et Phil.)
4. South Africa, *The Official Year Book of the Republic of South Africa* (11th edn). Department of Foreign Affairs, Pretoria, 1985, Section 5.
5. Vilakazi, H., 'Education in South Africa: exploring the roots of crisis', *UCT Alumni*, 1986, **1**, No. 8, 19.
6. Moulder, J., 'Black into White and White into Black. The quiet revolution in South African Universities'. University of Cape Town, 1985. (Paper presented to AGM of the Nederlands Zuidafrikaanse Vereniging.)
7. See reference 5.
8. See reference 2, pp. 8, 9.
9. Kok, P. C., 'Bevolkingsherversspreiding in die R.S.A.—moontlike lang-termyn implikasies van huidige tendense', *RGN Verslag S—86*, Pretoria, 1982.
10. See reference 2.
11. de Villiers, J. C. (ed.), *Report and recommendations of the Committee of Enquiry on possible further facilities for medical and dental training*. Government Printer, Pretoria, 1984, p. 16.
12. See reference 11, p. 17.
13. Van Rensburg, H. C. J. and Mans, A., *Profile of Disease and Health Care in South Africa*. Academica, Pretoria, 1982, p. 26.
14. See reference 11, p. 36.
15. South African Nursing Association, The Board, *Report on Nursing Education in the Republic of South Africa 1979–1983*. SANA, Pretoria, 1985, p. 20.
16. (a) South African Nursing Council, *Statistical returns for the calendar year 1986*. SANC, Pretoria, 1987 C2/M87(B) and C3/M87(D).
    (b) Thompson, R., 'Today's nursing for tomorrow's health', *Curationis*, 1986, **9**, No. 4.
17. See reference 15, p. 21.
18. See reference 11, p. 37.
19. See reference 11, pp. 114, 115.
20. See reference 16(a), C2/M87(B) and (J).
21. The word 'training' as used in South Africa does not have the same meaning as it has in the United States of America. Training and education are used synonymously. In South Africa we refer to university training in the same sense as it is used in the United Kingdom. It is in this manner that it is used in this chapter.
22. Brownlee, E. B. I., *The Nursing Student in the University of South Africa*. University of South Africa, Pretoria, 1982, p. 60. (Thesis DLitt et Phil.)
23. Searle, C., *The History of the Development of Nursing in South Africa 1652–1960*. The South African Nursing Association, Pretoria, 1965, pp. 74, 75.
24. See reference 23, pp. 143, 284.
25. See reference 23, p. 285.

26. See reference 23, pp. 167, 168.
27. Harrison, P. H., 'Withdrawal of the South African Nursing Association from the International Council of Nurses', *SA Nursing Journal*, 1973 (September), 7, 8.
28. See reference 23, pp. 240–245.
29. See reference 23, p. 341.
30. See reference 22, p. 66.
31. See reference 22, p. 67.
32. See reference 23, pp. 234–235.
33. Kotze, W. J., 'The South African Nursing Council. Aspects of its development 1944–1984', *Curationis*, 1985, **8**, No. 4, 9.
34. See reference 16(b), p. 2.
35. Strauss, S. A., 'The expanding role of the nurse: its legal base', *SA Practice Management*, 1982, **3**, No. 3, 21.
36. See reference 16(b), p. 2.
37. (a) See reference 23, p. 289.
    (b) South African Nursing Association, The Board, *Nursing Education in the Republic of South Africa 1914–1974*. SANA, Pretoria, 1976.
38. (a) See reference 37(b).
    (b) See reference 33, pp. 5–14.
39. (a) See reference 15, p. 32.
    (b) South African Nursing Council, *Statistical returns for the calendar year 1985*. SANC, Pretoria, 1986, C3/M86(D).
    (c) See reference 16, C3/M87(d).
40. (a) South African Nursing Council, *Report of the Fifth Council 1965–1970*. SANC, Pretoria, 1970, p. 53.
    (b) South African Nursing Council, *Report of the Sixth Council 1970–1975*. SANC, Pretoria, 1975, p. 58.
41. See reference 37(b), p. 104.
42. South African Nursing Council, *Report of the Seventh Council 1975–1979*. SANC, Pretoria, 1979, pp. 55, 63.
43. See reference 37(b), p. 16.
44. See reference 16(a), C2/M87(B).
45. Department of Health and Welfare, *Health Service Facilities Plan*. Department of Health and Welfare, Pretoria, 1984.
46. Searle, C., 'New dimensions—nursing education in the post-secondary education system in the Republic of South Africa', *Curationis*, 1983, **6**, No. 1, 4.
47. South African Nursing Council, *Report of the Eighth Council 1970–1984*. SANA, Pretoria, 1984, pp. 21–22.
48. See reference 37(b), pp. 120–121.
49. See reference 22.
50. See reference 13, pp. 145, 324–325.
51. Searle, C., 'Overview of nursing education in South Africa 1914–1964'. *SA Nursing Journal*, 1964, **3**, No. 9, 70.
52. See reference 37(b), pp. 34, 36, 89.
53. See reference 37(b), p. 104.
54. See reference 23, pp. 108–109.
55. See reference 51, p. 67.

56. See reference 51, p. 67.
57. See reference 40(a), p. 61.
58. See reference 37(b), p. 48.
59. Roscher, C., 'Psigiatriese verpleging in Suid Afrika—"noorsig" ', *SA Nursing Journal*, 1975, **62**, No. 3, 13.
60. See reference 37(b), pp. 73, 102, 109.
61. See reference 37(b).
62. See reference 59, p. 14.
63. Simons, M., 'Women's Centenary at U.C.T.', *UCT Alumni*, 1986, **1**, No. 7, 6.
64. See reference 63, p. 10.
65. See reference 22, p. 29.
66. See reference 46, p. 5.
67. See reference 37(b), p. 24.
68. See reference 23, p. 307.
69. See reference 37(b), p. 47.
70. See reference 37(b), pp. 17, 25.
71. University of Cape Town, *General rules for students*. University of Cape Town, 1987, p. 4.
72. University of Cape Town, Gazette, January 1986 (unpublished).
73. See reference 37(b), pp. 49, 53.
74. Carlyle, T. quoted in Cohen, J. M. and M. J., *Penguin Dictionary of Quotations*. Penguin Books, Harmondsworth, England, 1960, p. 99.
75. See reference 37(b), p. 49.
76. See reference 37(b), pp. 84, 100, 103.
77. See reference 37(b), p. 129.
78. South African Nursing Association, The Board, *Report on Nursing Education in the Republic of South Africa and the Self-Governing Territories*. SANA, Pretoria, 1978, pp. 4, 10, 11.
79. See reference 16(a), C3/M87(B) and (D).
80. (a) Hunt, B. N., 'The working life of a group of nurses', *Curationis*, 1981, **4**, No. 2, 55–56.
    (b) Van Niekerk, P., '30 Jaar van Graadopleiding', *Nursing RSA*, 1986, **1**, No. 2, 28–29.
81. See reference 40(a), pp. 78, 79.
82. Van Niekerk, J. G. P., 'Verpleegkunde: 30 jaar van Graadopleiding in Suid Afrika', *Human Sciences Research Council Research Bulletin*, 1986, **16**, No. 5, 33.
83. See reference 22.
84. du Plessis, D. J., 'A signpost not a mirror—the past has a pointer for the future', *UCT Alumni*, 1986, **1**, No. 8, 18.
85. See reference 11, p. 72.
86. See reference 23, p. 339.
87. See reference 16(b), pp. 1–8.
88. Nightingale, F., *Florence Nightingale to her Nurses*. Macmillan, New York, 1914.

Index

In order to assist the reader, a certain amount of cross referencing has been offered so that differences in the international use of certain terms may be identified.